D1225201

Bills of Material

STRUCTURED FOR EXCELLENCE

Dave Garwood

Dogwood Publishing Company, Inc.
111 Village Parkway, Building 2
Marietta, GA. 30067
(800) 368-7775

Bills of Material

Structured For Excellence

by Dave Garwood

Dogwood Publishing Company, Inc.
111 Village Parkway, Building 2
Marietta, GA 30067
(800) 368-7775

Bills of Material: Structured For Excellence
1988,1993,1995 Dogwood Publishing Company, Inc.
111 Village Parkway, Building 2
Marietta, GA 30067

First Printing, 1988
Second Printing, 1988
Third Printing, 1990
Fourth Printing, 1993
Fifth Printing, 1995

Text and Editing by Michael Bane
Cover Design by Rebecca Finkel

ISBN 0-0621118-9-9

Contents

Dedication

This book is dedicated to my mentor and most respected friend, the late Oliver Wight.

ACKNOWLEDGMENTS

I've come to the conclusion that no one person writes a book. Instead, the one person only collects the thoughts of many others and communicates them with a few additional thoughts of their own. That is certainly the case with this book. My client companies have been very kind to serve as my "laboratories," and I am deeply in debt to them. A few, but certainly not all, are cited in this book.

Ray Bacon and Dave Biggs at Bently Nevada Corporation; Vernon Wright and Ray Dollar at Blue Bird Body Company and John Bearden, Jerry Hastings and Dale Hendrix at Centrilift are a few of the people specifically quoted in this book. The people at Cooper Canada, Connaught Labs and Fisher Controls are among the many others who have contributed greatly to the knowledge I've been able to share with you in *Structured For Excellence.*

It's unfortunate that I can't list everyone and pass on the credit they deserve. These people are the unsung heroes who battle the specific issue every day and make the consultants of the world look good.

My associates have also been very influential and instrumental in keeping me on the right path and sharing their experiences to enhance this book.

Don Rice has provided many valuable insights for this latest update. Don's experience in teaching our bill of material class and his vast consulting experience have helped us keep **Structured For Excellence** on the cutting edge.

Michael Bane, a professional writer, has played a major role in translating my thoughts into interesting, readable text. Without Michael's sense of humor, tolerance for my constant changes and unparalleled skill in professional writing, this book would probably never have happened!

John Civerolo's thorough critique and tenacity led to a major rewrite of the original manuscript.

One of the greatest rewards of writing a book is the opportunity to document a special appreciation for your loved ones. My best friend and wife, Lynn, has always been extremely supportive of my professional endeavors, and a strong partner at my side, helping me take the mystique out of new ideas and getting them into an understandable language. My son, Bret, and daughter, Beth, have sacrificed a lot of time with their dad during my career while I bounced around the country doing "research." Special thanks, then, to my family.

FOREWORD

I began my career fresh out of college as a Mechanical Engineer. My first assignment was to spend several months at the drafting table. I envisioned my role as a "creator"—creating innovative designs of products for the future!

At that time, creating the bill of material was simply a necessary evil, the final step in the product design project that had to be done before I could be assigned to another project. A few years later, reality intruded into my ordered world. First, I discovered that the people in Manufacturing actually tried to build the product with the bill of material I had created. What a revelation! In subsequent years, my experience gave me an entirely different view of the role of a bill of material plays in running a manufacturing business.

A couple of years after being transferred to the Manufacturing department, I was assigned the vague task of exploring what system or approach was necessary to eliminate material shortages, pull us out of the end-of-the-month shipping cycle and, in general, bring order to chaos. My search repeatedly led me back to the bill of material as a prime player in resolving our problems. My first exposure to what is often called "CIM" (Computer Integrated Manufacturing) was a newly announced product from IBM called "BOMP" (Bill of Material Processor).

To my surprise, the bill processor was not a paper shredder! It was simply a computer program that allowed us to store, maintain and retrieve lists of material to manufacture an item. Although the bill processor is a powerful tool, it does not "structure" the bill of material. The next few years were spent in constant meetings struggling with the issues of how to "structure" the bill and feed the bill processor the proper data.

This experience led me to a greater appreciation for how critical the bill of material is to a company. Many critical decisions hang on how the bill is structured. Product costs, material availability, factory and vendor schedules, inventory investments and satisfied customers are just a few of the critical issues in a company that are significantly influenced by the bill of material structure.

The revolution in TQM (Total Quality Management) that has swept through American industry led us to the understanding that accurate, well-structured bills are a quality issue, part of the overall issue of quality.

During this early experience in my career, I did a few things right and a few things wrong. I still have scar tissue to testify to the latter! I soon realized that problems I was encountering were common to every manufacturing business, not unique to one company.

The next 25 years of my career have been spent working directly with over 1000 manufacturing companies, teaching courses on bill of material structuring to over 30,000 participants as well as giving presentations to thousands of additional people on the problems and solutions of structuring bills of material to help run a manufacturing company better. This book is a sharing of those years of experience and an exposure of the scar tissue I have accumulated. I think you'll find this book to be much more than just a book on the technical aspects of structuring bills of material. It's a book that gets into the many nitty-gritty issues in pursuit of becoming a World Class competitor.

We have "modularized" the content of the book to make it easier reading. The first section focuses on the issues an Executive Manager needs to know about bills of material. The next section gets into the details and focuses on the "how to." The last section focuses on implementation. We are confident you'll find the contents beneficial and helpful.

Dave Garwood
Atlanta, Georgia
1995

Section I

How To Use This Book

Bills of materials have been around for as long as there have been manufacturing companies. Undoubtedly, there have been problems with bills for at least that long.

At R.D. Garwood, Inc., we began teaching classes on bills of material in 1972. *Structured For Excellence* is the result of those classes and untold hours of consulting work.

Proper structuring of the bill has become even more critical in today's competitive world market. There is simply no leeway— we either work to World Class Performance standards, or we fail. As we move to meet those standards—implementing MRP II, moving to a Just-In-Time environment, making sure our quality is across-the-board up to par, looking at a computer-integrated future—it is vitally important that our groundwork, the bill of material, be solid.

By the way, in this book we often refer to World Class Performance. There are people who debate whether the term has been overused, and, no doubt, it's been misused as well. Still,

World Class Performance reflects a philosophy of "raising and meeting our customers' expectations faster than our competitors," and we don't feel that objective is debatable—it's essential to survival.

Structured For Excellence itself is structured in such a way as to provide the maximum benefit to you, the reader and user. The first section, Chapters One through Four, is basically an overview section. It will help you understand the role of the bill of material in a company, the basic concepts of structuring or restructuring a bill, and what the ramifications of bill problems really are. We'll also be showing you some solid examples of success with tough bill problems.

The purpose of Section One is to allow busy executives in to understand the basics of and the necessity for making sure the bill is up to par in accuracy and structure.

Section Two, Chapters Five through Sixteen, features the nuts and bolts chapters. Here's where we give you the knowledge and the tools necessary to get into the trenches with a bill and turn it into a competitive weapon.

Section Three, Chapters Seventeen through Nineteen, contains the implementation chapters. How do you get started on the road to excellent bills? How do you create the bill of material team, and who should be on that team? We'll also take a look at some do's and don'ts in software.

Bills Of Material: Structured For Excellence, then, is both a basic primer and a hands-on guide, allowing you to reach the greatest number of people in your company, giving you a solid jumpstart in the quest for World Class.

Good luck!

Chapter 1

The Bill of Material As A Quality Problem

What is a bill of material, anyway?

It seems like such an easy question. Walk through any factory, large or small, and ask anyone—a plant floor supervisor or a clerk in accounting—what is a bill of material, and, most likely, that person will have some kind of idea.

Or will they?

The problem with bills of material is precisely that they seem so simple: The bill of material is a list of the items to make a product. Seems simple enough, doesn't it. Yet, consider the company that had a major "bill of material" crisis after a bit of remodeling. Seems the *real* bill of material—the actual "recipe" for making the product—was written on a wall next to a machine. When the wall was moved, a critical company document got painted over.

We all know what the *real* bill of material is, right? It's the "secret" list we keep in the black book in our pocket. It's what's in Old Joe's head, since he's the only one who really knows what goes into what we make. It's Engineering's drawings, isn't it?

Let's go back to basics, starting with a definition. When we say "bill of material," we mean the company data that states what items or raw materials go into building or producing a product.

Every company has a bill of material. Some companies, especially chemical and food companies, may call them recipes; some have formulas; some have packaging specifications—all these terms mean the same thing, the items or the raw materials that go into producing the product.

After several years of teaching a class in structuring Bills of Material, we've come to one major conclusion—starting a discussion on how to structure a bill of material is a good way to start a fight in a bar.

> Beginning a discussion on how to structure the bill of material is a good way to start a fight in a bar...

The bill of material is a controversial topic. Who owns the bill? Who's responsible for updating the bill? How accurate does the bill have to be? What's wrong with the *old* system: Add-delete bills, separate engineering and manufacturing bills, parts lists on engineering drawings and little black books? And what about part numbers? Engineering changes? New product introductions? The problem is made that much worse by confusing terminology—product structure, planning bills, configurators and the like.

The Bill's Role

The reason any discussion of the bill of material is a heated discussion is because the bill of material is central to a company. Materials are ordered based on the bill; product cost is calculated from the bill. Production and supplier schedules are all tied to the bill, which means, in short, that many of the company's resources are committed based on the bill of material.

Recently, however, the bill of material has been under increased scrutiny. The advent of formal business management systems such as Manufacturing Resource Planning (MRP II) has focused new light on the bill of material. Just-In-Time (JIT), sometimes called continuous flow manufacturing, has added a new focus on implications of the B/M structure. In order for any formal planning and scheduling system to work, the bill of material *must be complete and accurate*. Not accurate as in written on the wall next to a machine; not accurate as in notations in a black book, but demonstrably, certifiably accurate in the database for everyone in the company to use.

As more and more businesses have re-engineered their processes to benefit from these formal systems, the bill of material has become a major stumbling block.

There is a fear of changing how the bill of material is structured, partly based on the idea that the old bill worked just fine. The people who originally helped structure the bill have a certain pride of authorship. They're not exactly enthused about changing the bill, since that implies their original structure was *wrong* somehow. There are a lot of parochial viewpoints involved, each department certain that *its bill of material is the real* bill of material.

Let's challenge some of the existing paradigms on bills of material by answering three simple questions:

• Who uses the bill of material?

Figure 1: B/M Users

• Who's the most important user of the bill of material?

• Who's the most demanding user of the bill of material?

Just a little thought gives us the obvious answer to the first question—everybody in the company uses the bill of material.

No single area of the company "owns" the bill.

That may come as a shock to some Engineering departments, who have a proprietary feeling for the bill. That's not surprising, since Engineering created the first bill for the product.

"In our case, Engineering had taken control of the bill," says Dave Biggs of Bently Nevada. "It was theirs. And they could have cared less how Manufacturing built the product; whether the bill really reflected how things were done on the plant floor."

The reason Engineering wanted to retain control of the bill was a common one—Engineering was afraid that if it didn't have sole control of the bill, Manufacturing would make changes in the bill that would have long-term engineering or product liability repercussions.

"There were good intentions there. There always are," says Biggs, himself an engineer. "The problem is, the end result was disastrous. Over a period of years we had demonstrated that even if Manufacturing requested a change in the bill, we wouldn't make it. So Manufacturing made their own bill of material, and it happened to be documented on a corkboard in the stockroom."

Obviously, Manufacturing uses the bill of material to build the product. If it doesn't have access to the "real" bill of material, it'll make their own. The bill is also used to help determine routings, that is, how to make the product.

The stockroom has to use the bill to issue the items.

The Planning Department uses the bill of material to schedule the materials that make up the product.

Finance and accounting uses the bill to cost the product.

Order entry uses the bill of material to help configure the product. The Service Department needs the bill to know which service parts go into the product. Finally, Quality Assurance uses the bill to assure the product is made properly.

These are the "customers" of the bill of material structuring process. Each customer has his or her own expectations for the "product" of the process, in this case the bill of material itself.

Everyone wants the bill structured to suit his or her own needs, and that's why the fight starts.

All these various customers—the different departments—have a legitimate right to the bill of material. Since no department "owns" the bill, who is the most important customer?

There is no most important customer of the bill of material. There is, however, a most demanding customer.

Some departments can tolerate generalities: Engineering, for example, can specify using an item "as required," say, in the case of washers or small screws. Cost accounting might simply refer to the required material as "steel," while Purchasing needs to know the size, shape and type of steel. When you engineer a product, you don't adjust the tolerances for the lightest use the product is likely to see. Rather, you build for the toughest use—you build to meet the needs of the most demanding customer. It's exactly the same with the bill of material. The bill must be structured to fill the needs of the most demanding customer, the Planning Department.

Planning is not more important than any of the other customers of the bill of material. It's just that they demand a higher level of accuracy than most of the other customers. The part numbers must be correct. The bill must be properly structured. All the information must be accurate. When we talk about the total quality of the bill, that includes the accuracy and the structure.

The bill must also meet the expectations of all the customers, and don't those customers—all the people in the company who use the bill—expect the bill of material to be accurate and correctly structured?

While the bill must be structured to satisfy Planning's more demanding expectations, all the other users of the bill have legitimate needs for the data. They don't, however, need to see the data in the same form or detail as Planning. In fact, each individual department has its own special pattern or, template, for using the data contained in the bill of material database.

Our objective must be to have a single company bill of material database that provides multiple views to support the needs of all the users. This is a fundamental principle of our bill of material process.

There is another aspect to bill of material problems from the quality arena. We have traditionally thought of quality exclusively in terms of *product quality*—does the product work. Are the shakes, rattles, blemishes and scratches totally absent? Is the product defect-free? The concept of Total Quality Management (TQM) encompasses a number of things beyond product quality. Was, for instance, the product delivered on time? Was the same item delivered that the customer ordered? Did the customer receive perceived value? Phil Crosby's definition of quality as "conformance to requirements" was a major step toward helping us realize the true meaning of the "total" in Total Quality Management. But in today's competitive global market, that definition could mislead us into focusing only on conforming to the specifications rather than the *total* customer expectations. We prefer, then, to refer to quality as "conformance to all the customer's expectations."

> There is a fear of changing how the bill of material is structured–partly based on the idea that the old bill worked just fine...

External customers—the ones who send us the checks for products and services—clearly have expectations we must meet. We also have *internal* customer expectations. The internal customers are the ones who receive the output of various "suppliers" in the processes required to run our businesses. Clearly, in any organization, there are many bill of material "customers." For example, the plant floor needs a list of items to make the product. The Service Department and the Cost Accounting Department need to know what went into the product. The bill of material should be the single database of information to meet all of those needs or expectations. But when the internal customer expectations aren't met, the internal customers create, and then have to maintain, their own bills of material. The result is redundant, expensive maintenance tasks--often of incorrect information!

And the list of bill of material customers is quite long in any company. When those expectations are not met, the problem, by definition, becomes a quality problem—noncomformance to expectations. And while some customers may have differing expectations, they all have one thing in common—the need for accuracy.

What happens when the expectations aren't met?

Well, the business doesn't stop functioning. Each of the users begins building subsystems or informal systems to meet the individual needs. Sometimes, this takes the form of separate bills of material, pads or cushions of inventory, or forcing the customer to wait while they compensate for the nonconformances. All of these costs and activities are nonvalue-adding. Therefore, attacking all of these nonconformances provides an excellent opportunity to reduce costs and speed our response to meeting external customer expectations. These nonconformances directly reflect poor quality in the business process of structuring and maintaining bills of material.

Process, Not People

This is not, let us emphasize, a "people" problem. It's a process problem.

So why haven't we taken advantage of these opportunities to reduce costs and increase speed before now? A major reason is that these costs and delays are often not readily visible and certainly not directly attributed to the bill of material structuring process. So the opportunities are overlooked.

Can we afford a high-quality bill of material structuring process? The answer is we can't afford not to have one. The costs and delays of not conforming to all of the internal customer expectations is enormous.

The Cost Of Non-Conformance

Bill of material problems sometimes are tricky to diagnose, but they translate into big problems—and big bucks—for any company. When there are problems with the bill, it's hard to make or buy the right items in the right quantity at the right time. That leads to:

- *Missed customer deliveries.* You can't service your customers if you can't make and deliver the product on time.
- *Too much inventory.* The fear that the only way to keep the production lines running is stockpiling materials, which translates into dollars sitting in the warehouse.
- *Inefficient production.* When the wrong items, or the wrong number of items, are delivered to the plant floor, manufacturing scrambles to compensate.

> The more bills there are scattered throughout the company, the harder it is to maintain them all accurately...

- *The cost of doing business is too high.* Extra money being spent for unnecessary inventory; expediters dashing here and there trying to overcome shortages and get product out the door; increased costs of maintaining both Engineering and Manufacturing bills. Not the best way to do business.
- *Lack of teamwork and communication.* Who wants to work hard for the team when some of the other team members are boobs? Can't even deliver the right material to run the equipment...
- *Frustration and poor morale.* People basically want to do a good job. They want to meet their quotas, and they want their company to be successful. Speaking from experience, nothing is more frustrating than not having the right items to do your job. It doesn't take many frustrations like that to sour morale at a basically good company.
- *Wasted resources.* There are five critical resources: People, materials, equipment, money and the constraint of time. Think of resources as silver bullets. You only have a limited number of them, so you have to call your shots carefully. Wasting capacity or wasting time is no different than wasting money. You've squandered a portion of your silver bullets.

One of the basic steps toward making good use of our resources is careful structuring of the bill of material.

A New Look

Before we discuss how to structure the bill, first we need to look at the bill a slightly different way. Many bill of material problems have sprung from the very fact that the bill is used throughout the company. And everywhere it's used, it *looks* different, something we'll be going into detail about later on. The Engineering parts list looks, or is structured, differently than the pick list Manufacturing uses to issue material to build the product. The pick list is different from the document Finance uses to cost out the product. Planning and Scheduling uses yet another different version of the bill. It is easy to think of each of these variations of the bill as separate documents, each one the "real" bill of material.

This is the way many companies operate!

In fact, all the different bills should be nothing but sorted versions of the main company bill of material, what we call the Master Bill of Material, a single company database.

The Master Bill of Material is the company database for a particular product or family of products. We use the term database because, realistically, the Master Bill of Material is stored in the computer. The Master Bill is the only "real" bill of material. When the master scheduler needs a planning bill or the plant floor needs a pick list, those two documents should be generated from the Master Bill of Material. If anyone inside or outside the company has a question about what parts or ingredients or components went into a certain product, the Master Bill of Material should answer that question.

The advantages to such a system are tremendous. Consider maintaining the bill of material. Even well-structured bills have crumpled under the weight of constant maintenance. The more bills there are scattered throughout the company, the harder it is to maintain them all accurately. Engineering is working on

Revision "Z", while the plant floor is still working from Revision "B". Costs are being figured on Revision "C", and no one in the company can figure out why the product isn't getting produced, but is costing more than projected. A single Master Bill of Material is much easier to maintain. It's also much easier to handle configuration control from a single Master Bill. Configuration control, something we'll be talking about throughout this book, is becoming more and more of a critical issue. Basically, it means knowing what was supposed to and what actually did go into your product. Chemical, drug and food companies, as well as companies working for the government, have always had to have traceability for what went into the product. Obvious examples are cases of drug contamination. The drug companies involved must be able to tie the specific lot of ingredients used to specific order numbers. In the present litigious atmosphere in America, where product liability suits are a way of life, you had better know exactly what is in your product. The continued existence of your company may someday hinge on that information.

Formal Versus Informal

Formal business management systems demand an accurate bill of material. There are tremendous benefits to be gained from a formal system such as MRP II, including better productivity, better customer service *and* lower costs. The only catch is that a formal system requires accuracy and maintenance to keep on working.

We're all familiar with the old, informal systems. We were once brought in to consult for a company who saw market share slipping and wanted to tighten up its procedures. When I asked to see the bill of material, they referred me to Eldon, who'd apparently been there since the creation of the company or the dawn of time. When I asked Eldon about the bill, he pulled a wad of papers from the back pocket of his coveralls, consulted the grimy papers and proceeded to recite what went into each product. When I asked about engineering changes, I was referred to Eldon. Inventory?

Eldon. Purchasing? Eldon knew what to order.

When the company asked me for recommendations, I suggested that they pay Eldon whatever he wanted and pick him up and drive him home in an armored truck.

Anyone in manufacturing has similar stories. And, to be truthful, in a period of no competition, the informal system works just fine. When competition heats up, though, and more production, shorter customer lead times and new products are needed to stay competitive, the informal system starts breaking down. There's no accurate way of figuring what parts are needed when. New product introductions are nothing short of wholesale chaos, and Eldon decides that now would be a good time to retire.

> "Making changes in a manufacturing company is probably the hardest thing that civilized man has ever set out to achieve."
> –J. Chris Horrock, 1890

A formal system, on the other hand, is designed to expand as needed. A well-structured bill of material can simplify planning woes, keep the production line moving and ease new product introduction. It must, however, be accurate. A formal system like MRP II uses the Master Bill of Material for all planning and scheduling. If the bill is not accurate, MRP II will plan and schedule items that are not needed, wasting money, or not plan and schedule needed items, wasting time and capacity. MRP II is a powerful tool, but without an accurate Master Bill of Material, it is a tool that will not work. Similarly, JIT and Computer Integrated Manufacturing (CIM) begin with the assumption that the basics, such as bill of material accuracy, are in place.

"Making changes in a manufacturing company is probably the hardest thing that civilized man has ever set out to achieve," wrote J. Chris Horrock. He wrote that in 1890, and the situation hasn't changed that much since then.

We will, though, through the course of this book, be looking at manufacturing companies that have changed their ways and are benefiting from the changes.

Bently Nevada builds electronic test equipment; the Blue Bird Body Co. builds school buses; Centrilift, A Baker-Hughes Co., supplies pumps for oil wells and APCOM makes thermostats and heating elements for water heaters. Connaught Labs is a drug manufacturer, and Cooper Canada makes, among other things, hockey gloves. What they have in common is a willingness to change, to make themselves more competitive in an increasingly competitive worldwide marketplace. Each of these companies also found that the bill of material was the centerpiece of the company changes.

"When we started," says Dave Biggs, senior vice president at Bently Nevada, "we didn't have an accurate bill. In fact, the `bill' was actually a bunch of notes on a corkboard. There was a bill of material file, sure. But you'd get the bill of material file, then you'd frantically go look for the piece of paper that had the revisions on it so you knew what to really pull."

The problems can be solved.

Discussion Points

1. Discuss the definition of "quality" and what it means in your business.

2. Identify and list all of the internal and external customers of your bill of material structuring and maintenance process.

3. Who are the internal and external customers of your bill of material? List them.

4. What are the expectations of each of your bill of material customers? List them.

5. Which of the expectations of your bill of material customers are not currently being met?

6. What are the costs, both tangible and intangible, of not meeting the expectations of your bill of material customers?

Chapter 2

Ten Critical Issues

Before a bill of material can be restructured, there are basic questions that must be addressed, such as what are the rules for assigning part numbers or what should be included on or excluded from the bill of material?

There are other questions, though, that don't fall into the nuts and bolts category but are every bit as important—maybe more important—as the "how-to" questions.

Those questions center around the idea of how we want to run our business.

Remember, there's no "correct" way to structure the bill of material. The bill must support the manufacturing process, not dictate it. Accordingly, the bill structure must look at ten critical issues:

1. Customer lead time versus manufacturing lead time
2. What items to forecast and master schedule
3. The manufacturing process itself, including methods, production costs and material flow
4. Production costs
5. The volume of paperwork and inventory transactions
6. Bill of material maintenance
7. Inventory investment

8. Design considerations
9. Order entry requirements
10. Documentation

These issues tend to be interdependent. The challenge is to find the proper trade-off solutions to resolve these issues.

For instance, let's take a look at the interdependence of the manufacturing process, bill maintenance and documentation. Suppose we are working in a traditional factory. We see our international competition increasing, and we know that to remain competitive—indeed, to survive—we are going to have to run the business better. We decide on an approach that includes elements of MRP II, JIT and Total Quality Management (TQM).

One of the first things, though, is to clean up the bills. We want to make sure they are accurate and correctly structured. After a massive effort and many months of agony, we are finally sure our bills are accurate and properly structured.

Then we change the manufacturing process to a more con-tinuous flow environment using work cells or start using Kanban to trigger Work-In-Process (WIP) replenishments. Materials pre-viously inventoried at WIP points are now eliminated. Some levels of the bill are no longer be needed. The documentation, such as drawings or test specs, may be different.

Are our bills still correctly structured?

Maybe, but, more likely, maybe not.

We have changed the manufacturing process, which has probably created the need to alter the structure of the bill. We have very possibly put ourselves in the situation of having to do the hard work of structuring the bill over again. Of course, it may not take as long this time, but the point is we must look at the overall questions before we start to work on the nitty gritty details.

A Cheesy Example

Let's look at a more detailed example of how these issues are interrelated, starting with the relationship between manufacturing lead time and customer delivery lead time. Or are we going to forecast and manufacture to a certain level, then assemble or finish the product to customer order? Are we going to build to a forecast and put the finished product on a shelf before we get the order? Questions like these are central to the bill restructuring, and the answers expand out in all directions.

An example we use in class is a pizza. For years a pizza restaurant in our neighborhood has watched its lunch crowd be eaten away by the fast food outlets. Customer expectations were changing rapidly, and what the fast food outlets could offer that our pizza palace couldn't was *speed*, in and out in just a few minutes. In response, our pizza palace began offering a lunch pizza, ready in five minutes or your next meal free.

> It's a question of what kind of business we actually are...

However, we couldn't get *every* conceivable pizza on the menu in five minutes. There were just too many combinations of onions, mushrooms, anchovies and other goodies. Instead, the pizza joint created three "standards"—cheese, cheese and pepperoni or the "deluxe."

Suppose we went in and ordered a five-minute pizza, only instead of pepperoni, we wanted ground beef. And anchovies and green peppers.

Could we get that pizza in five minutes, please?

The answer is an emphatic "No." There are only three choices for quickie pizza, not because our restaurant is stingy with its pizza toppings, but rather because the lead time to manufacture such a pizza was longer than five minutes. There are hundreds of toppings, thousands of combinations. Bringing one of each kind of pizza to a "semi-finished" level would involve a pizza parlor only slightly smaller than Italy.

There are several issues involving how our neighborhood restaurant chose to run the business. Let's imagine ourselves as the CEO of our pizza restaurant and step through the questions:

Because of the competition from fast food restaurants, the customers are unwilling to wait for a "traditional" pizza. The manufacturing lead time is now much longer than the customer expected delivery time. This leads to the next alternative. To respond to our competition, we can build to a forecast and stock the pizzas. Customers can then come in and choose their pizzas "off the shelf."

No problem, except that customers seem to have a problem with cold, hard pizzas with congealed cheese on top. That's not to mention the problems with stocking 10,000 individual pizza types!

In other words, building to stock would create unacceptable end item quality problems and a huge inventory of different pizzas.

As an alternative, then, let's *semi-finish*, or bring to a subassembly level, pizzas. Then, rather than making to stock, we can finish to customer order.

In order to make the five-minute deadline, though, we must take another step. We know that it's physically impossible for our three high school cooks to produce a pizza even from a semi-finished state in five minutes if they've got to run all over the restaurant looking for Spanish olives, Romano cheese, anchovies and jalapeno peppers.

In fact, to make that five minute deadline, we have to set up a special section of the kitchen and assign a dedicated cook for just the five-minute pizza. Maybe we'll call that a work cell.

To make this mini-assembly line work, we create the three "standards"—cheese, cheese and pepperoni and deluxe—available in five minutes. These standards are processed through the new work center, finished to customer order from the semi-finished pizzas.

The entire other menu is available, of course, if the customer is willing to wait the complete manufacturing lead time. In effect, before the restructuring, there was a bill of material for each individual pizza, and the bill had only one level. Now, the semi-finished pizza has a part number, and an additional level in the bill is created. There's more bill of material maintenance, but it's necessary both to keep the customers happy and to minimize inventory. That's the trade-off.

Forecasting And Planning

The next issue is one of forecasting and planning.

Our pizza parlor has, in effect, created bills of material for the three five-minute semi-finished pizzas. To decide on which pizzas to offer in five minutes, they used research into customer preferences. That research discovered that of 100 pizzas baked, 10 percent of those pizzas were cheese, 20 percent pepperoni and 30 percent deluxe. The 40 percent balance wanted one (or more) of the hundreds of other toppings. The reason we can get the pizza in five minutes is that they're already "in production" before we ever order.

The management of the restaurant has made a series of critical decisions about the way they want to run the business: That they would forgo options that would lengthen the manufacturing lead time to meet customer lead time expectations; that they would create non-traditional work cells to help achieve the goal of competitiveness; that they would structure their bills of material to make those changes possible.

We must deal with all those basic questions if we are to survive in a world market.

How much inventory do we want or can afford to keep on hand? Say we make six hundred different types of Custom Widgets, and the manufacturing lead time on the widgets is six weeks. Because of a volatile market, the customer expects to be able to receive his or her Custom Widget in six *hours*. Customers are notoriously unpredictable, so we're not sure how many of the six hundred varieties of widgets we're likely to sell. How can we make sure we always have all six hundred varieties of Custom Widgets available to sell?

One perfectly legitimate way is to give each Custom Widget a part number and a bill of material, then make lots and lots of all six hundred varieties of Custom Widgets and put them in inventory. When a customer order comes in, we can just pull the appropriate Custom Widget off the shelf and sell it.

What's the drawback here?

Money, tied up in the form of inventory. How much money

are we willing to tie up in inventory? Is the inventory there because it's necessary, or is it there because, "That's the way we've always done business"? There's also lots of additional costs for maintaining bills for all 600 varieties—necessary if we choose to run our business this way.

The alternative is a "pizza" solution, keep inventory at a semi-finished level. Obviously, to do so we have to understand the impact on the 10 Critical Issues such as manufacturing processes and costs. The answers to these questions can have profound impact on our traditional businesses.

What kind of business are we? Process, make-to-order (or, as they say, invent-to-order), job shop? Sometimes the answer isn't as clear as you'd think—you'll see real-world examples in future chapters. We may consider ourselves a certain type of industry when, in fact, the way we manufacture the product might point in another direction. If we make to stock, that is, make the end items and place them in inventory, how and where do we get our forecasts regarding future sales. Do we finish to customer order, as in the pizza example? Our bill structure, of course, needs to reflect the way we manufacture our product.

How much paperwork can we (or are we willing to) put up with? This is another critical question, because even the best system can be killed by excessive paperwork. Many companies' initial attempts at restructuring the bill have floundered in useless paperwork. In terms of bill structure, more levels in the bill usually require more paperwork and inventory transactions.

Finally, and this is very important: *We need to evaluate the bill structure in light of changing the manufacturing processes.* It is the manufacturing process itself that dictates when part numbers are needed and the structure of the bill itself.

The Traditional Flow

Take a look at the bill of material for our Model Z instrument (Figure 1, next page).

The planning for the Model Z instrument starts at the top and works its way down through each level of the bill of material.

MODEL Z INSTRUMENT

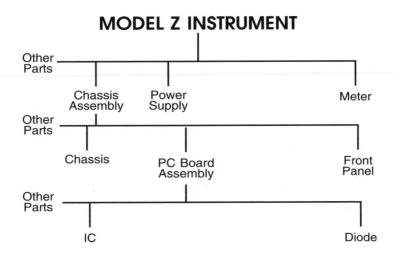

Figure 1: The Model Z Instrument

Execution starts at the bottom and works its way up. In other words, as parts become available, each of the lower level subassemblies are built, and, finally, the top level assembly—the Model Z instrument—is completed. Inventory planners release orders or schedules for each of the subassemblies when the component parts are available. The technique of using the master schedule, the bill of material and the inventory records to calculate requirements and trigger the release of work orders is called Material Requirements Planning.

The physical flow of material in the traditional production process to build the Model Z instrument is shown in Figure 2.

(Note that MRP didn't dictate or mandate this flow or bill structure. MRP did provide a way to manage it if we decide to do it this way).

Printed circuit

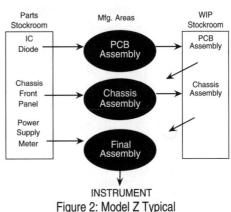

Figure 2: Model Z Typical

board (PCB) assemblies are produced in some economic order quantity and moved to a work-in-process stockroom when completed. The inventory planners release orders for chassis assemblies when the printed circuit board assembly and the components stored in the parts stockroom are available. The chassis assemblies are also built in some economic order quantity and stored in the work-in-process stockroom when they are finished. Work orders for instruments are released when all parts are available and moved to Finished Goods Inventory. Notice that the bill of material has been structured to match the physical flow of material for the Model Z instrument. Each subassembly has a part number and a bill of material.

Several options are available for the Model Z instrument. For example, several ranges of frequency, each requiring a different diode. The instrument is available with different sensitivity ranges, each requiring a different IC. Several different and unique printed circuit board assemblies can be built based on the numerous combinations of frequency range and sensitivity options in the instrument. Different configurations of the front panel also create numerous unique chassis assemblies. Each printed circuit board assembly and chassis assembly has its own part number and bill of material. When the work order is released by the inventory planner, a pick list is printed. The stockroom uses the pick list to issue component parts for each unique assembly. Once built, the subassembly goes into the work-in-process stockroom. All this activity requires paperwork transactions for issuing and receiving material in and out of stockrooms. The variety of unique printed circuit boards and chassis assemblies also puts a strain on maintaining high quality. Each one must be tested for its unique characteristics. Additional paperwork transactions are also required for tracking labor for each operation within the printed circuit board, chassis assembly and final assembly areas. Bills of material for each of the numerous unique subassemblies are also maintained in the computer files.

All of these tasks add cost and stretch out the time it takes to manufacture the product. It takes a lot of time to release work orders at each level, issue material, manufacture the subassemblies, put them in inventory and later draw them back out. Are these tasks necessary? Unless we change the manufacturing process—as we should—they are indeed necessary.

The bills weren't structured this way because of MRP II, JIT, CFM, Kanban or any other acronym. The bill of material structure didn't dictate the method of manufacturing. Actually, the reverse is true. The bill of material has been structured to comply with the method of manufacturing and material flow. Obviously, the current product design and manufacturing flow presents several opportunities for eliminating costly, time-consuming tasks..

After a lot of hard work, the Model Z instrument has been streamlined and is now manufactured in an ideal flow. Look at the revised material flow for the Model Z (Figure 3).

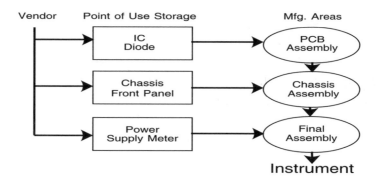

Figure 3: Revised Material Flow

Setup times in the printed circuit board assembly and chassis assembly area have been significantly reduced, making it economical to manufacture only as many as required, not an economic order quantity. The quantity required depends on the number of instruments needed—sometimes one, sometimes one hundred. The product has been redesigned, with many of the option-sensitive components standardized. Some of the option-sensitive parts have been moved to the end of the process and are now added as part of the final assembly operation. This means far less variety of printed circuit boards and chassis assemblies. It also means fewer bills of material, with less costs to maintain the bill.

Printed circuit board assemblies are now immediately consumed in chassis assembly and passed on to final assembly in the same day, or a small WIP inventory is maintained. In this case, *Kanban* (demand pull) replaces the material requirements planning technique to order printed circuit board and chassis subassemblies, which means the number of inventory planners has been reduced.

It's important to note, however, that material requirements planning is still used to plan the purchased parts. Pick lists are no longer used. Material is issued in bulk from the parts stockroom to the point-of-use locations in the production areas. A technique called *backflushing* is used to reduce on-hand inventory balances of components. The WIP stockroom has disappeared, and a perpetual inventory record isn't needed. Overhead costs have been reduced because the volume of transactions to maintain inventory records has been minimized.

Because order quantities have been significantly reduced, manufacturing lead time has also been significantly reduced. In fact, it's now possible to build the printed circuit board assemblies, chassis assemblies and the instrument to customer order rather than to forecast. The bill of material is now configured to customer order, not created and maintained for every possible Model Z.

All the uncertainty in the demand for printed circuit board and chassis subassemblies has been eliminated. The work-in-process stockroom has disappeared.

Since the manufacturing process has been revised and streamlined, the bill of material must also change. The bill is now flattened (See Figure 4). We call this a *shallow* bill of material.

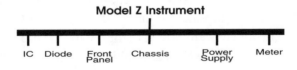

Figure 4: The Flattened Model Z B/M

Remember: The bill of material structure wasn't "wrong" before, any more than the present structure is "right." The key is to understand the impact on paperwork, inventory transactions, product costs, forecasting, manufacturing lead times and other elements affected as the manufacturing processes change. The bill of material cannot be changed to the more desirable shallow bill until the *process* has been changed. Manufacturing methods must be capable of adding option-sensitive items later in the process *without* adding significant costs or compromising quality. Manufacturing lead times must be reduced before the subassemblies can be made to order. Setup times must be reduced before lot sizes are made smaller, allowing the subassemblies to be immediately consumed, eliminating the need for an additional part number and tracking in and out of work-in-process stockrooms. Now, instead of forecasting instruments, we can use *planning bills* to forecast part requirements and build the instrument to customer order.

And, of course, all this must be accomplished without a cost penalty.

Sales, Order entry, Manufacturing, Engineering, the shop floor, Production Control, Accounting, the stockrooms and Product Engineering are all affected by these changes. Each and every one of these departments must understand *why* the manufacturing process is changing, the impact of those changes on the bill structure and—very importantly—how those changes will affect their jobs.

This is why all those people need to participate in bill of material structuring.

It's equally important to recognize the elements of the system that are still necessary. Although the number of levels in the bill of material has changed, the necessity of an accurate bill has not diminished. A valid master schedule is still an essential ingredient. Accurate inventory records for point-of-use and the parts stockroom are still required. Drawings and specifications for the subassemblies may still be necessary, although part numbers are not required. Changing the manufacturing process and restructuring the bills hasn't affected these crucial elements.

So now we've moved from the typical manufacturing process to the ideal process. Lots of things have had to change for us to get there, and lots of people had to be involved. In the real world, maybe the bill never gets perfectly flat; maybe the manufacturing process can never be totally changed to the ideal process. But each step helps! For example, if the setup time for the printed circuit board can't be reduced economically for another two years, the PCBs may be built in larger quantities than immediately needed and put into a stockroom. A part number and another level in the bill is required until the setup time is reduced.

In reality, the bill is always being revised to keep it in step with the manufacturing process. As we move toward ideal, there's less money tied up in inventory, and less lead time, which translates into a faster response time to customer needs. This is an example of JIT, (or CFM or whatever you choose to call the process) which moves away from grouping by function to grouping by work cells, arranged so the work flows from beginning to end without going back into inventory. JIT works hand-in-hand with a restructuring of the bills of material.

In some cases, it may be impossible for you to get down to a single level bill of material for an entire product. The important point is that the bill *mirrors* the process, not the other way around.

It's important to note here that these techniques work just as well for a product that isn't assembled. Figure 5 shows the material flow in a non-assembled environment, in this case a company that manufactures bags for potato chips. Notice that the process and opportunities are the same as the Model Z instrument.

Also notice the interdependence of

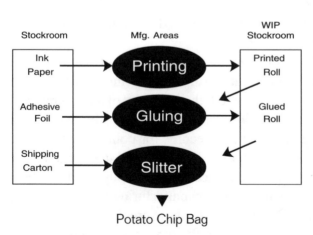

Figure 5: Flow For A Non-Assembled Product

the 10 Critical Issues was we move from the Traditional to the Ideal flow. Instruments or bags, the shorter manufacturing lead time now makes it possible to consider changing from a make-to-order business to a make-to-forecast business. Finished goods inventory is eliminated. Of course, product design may have to change to make it all possible—and the interdependence goes on and on.

Understanding the interdependence and, more importantly, the opportunities for improving our competitive advantages is essential for everyone. Especially, though, for Executive Management. While this isn't solely a bill of material issue, examining the process of structuring the bills is a good way to surface these opportunities.

Discussion Points

1. Are you a make-to-order or a make-to-forecast business? Discuss examples of each in your business and the implications of making to forecast rather than to order, and vice-versa.

2. Using the pizza parlor example, discuss the impact of changing the customer delivery lead time on the manufacturing lead time. Also discuss the impact throughout the organization of the alternative approaches to meeting short customer delivery times.

3. Select one product and discuss the opportunities for reducing inventory investment while simultaneously improving customer service if the product was made to customer order instead of to a sales forecast. What is the impact on the bill of material structure?

4. Using the flow diagram in Figure #2, change the names of the material and manufacturing areas to reflect one of your products. What is the impact as you consider each of the Ten Critical Issues as you move from the Traditional Flow in Figure #2 to the Ideal Flow in Figure #3?

5. What is the connection between the Ten Critical Issues and a Total Quality Management Program?

Chapter 3

"If It Ain't Broke..."

We've all heard it before, maybe one of the oldest adages in business—"If it ain't broke, don't fix it..." In the new world of World Class competition, though, maybe the proper way to read this is, "If you're not fixing it, it's broke!" JIT, CFM, TQM, "re-engineering," and CIM have presented new challenges on the road to World Class Performance—in some cases, challenges that directly apply to traditional material flow on the plant floor. By establishing work cells or changing the material flow, we directly affect the bill of material.

The bill must support the manufacturing process, a mirror of the way the product is manufactured. As we challenge our manufacturing processes—and we must challenge them if we're to become a World Class competitor—we must look back at the bill of material. This doesn't mean that the old bill of material was wrong—only that it might no longer support the revised manufacturing process. We need to go looking, then, both for problems in the bill, such as accuracy problems, and problems in structure.

We pointed out earlier that many problems in a company trace back to the bill of material. Sometimes, though, it's hard to point at a problem and say flatly that it's the result of a bill of material problem.

There are some danger signs, though, that your company should be watching for. If any of these signs exist, your bill may need work.

The first and foremost sign is the presence of numerous bills of material databases. Finding a bill of material in a manufacturing company isn't a problem. In many companies, deciding which one to use is the problem. Engineering issues new or revised bills, and the other departments update them as the spirit moves them. And on the plant floor, each foreman has a little black book with the real bill used to build the product. Each department exists in a vacuum, not communicating with other departments.

The "Silo Effect" can hinder, even totally block, the communication process...

"I've been involved in manufacturing for some 26 years," says Dale Hendrix of Centrilift. "In nearly all the companies I've worked for, Engineering owns the bills. They're Engineering bills, and it doesn't matter whether you use them in Manufacturing or wherever. There's nothing wrong with that philosophy, except that it's not true. It's like a bank—a bank has your money, but it's not theirs. That philosophy just doesn't provide the needs for managing a company the way a company has to be managed today."

"One of the biggest problems in Manufacturing," says Ray Bacon of Bently Nevada, "is that Manufacturing assumes incorrectly that the Engineering people know what we in Manufacturing can make and what we can't make. We're often dealing with a young group of engineers; we have 25 engineers who've been with the company less than three years. Most of them have zero experience in Manufacturing. In fact, most went through four years of engineering school and were never told that some engineers work in manufacturing. So Manufacturing people have traditionally made an assumption that the Engineering people knew what we can do and what we can do well and what we can't do. In reality, that's so far away from the truth that it isn't even in the ballpark."

We call this the "Silo Effect," each department resembling those towering silos of grain scattered throughout the Midwest. Those silos are surrounded by sturdy walls, which inhibit—or even totally stop—the communication process.

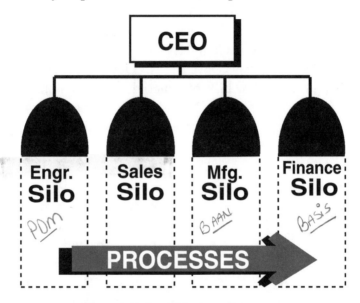

Figure 1: Horizontal Business Processes

The story's the same from every other departmental silo. They have their own bill of material, which is the *real* bill of material, and the folks from those other silos are nothing but barbarians hammering at the gates. Before you can begin a wholesale restructuring of the bill, communications channels have to be opened up between departments. Even if you're the president and CEO of the company, you can not *order* the Engineering department or the plant floor to give up its old, informal bills of material. Well, you can order, but all you'll succeed in doing is creating a sort of bill of material underground. The various departments must understand not only what the company is trying to accomplish, but also how high the stakes really are.

When that cooperation happens, though, the results are nothing short of astonishing.

When Bently Nevada faced its corkboard bill of material, Engineering figured it would take 50 man-years to update and correct the bills of material. Management enlisted Manufacturing's help, figuring that since it built the products, it probably knew what went into them. All the notes were pulled off the corkboard, and as products were needed, Manufacturing issued "corrected" bills of material. That's what was fed into the computer.

"Effectively, we made it easy for Manufacturing to update any bill of material," says Dave Biggs. "Out of self-defense, they made them right." New bills of material evolved naturally from this simple procedure. Bently Nevada's bills of material were 90-plus percent accurate within three-to-four months.

> We want to move to a single company B/M that satisfies all the internal customers' needs...

Six Key B/M Principles

We want to move from multiple bill of material databases to a single company bill of material database that satisfies all the internal customers. The problem isn't hopeless. The companies that have gone through the process have succeeded because they have followed six key principles:

1) Data in the part number and bill of material records is complete enough to satisfy the needs of every internal customer in the company, including Engineering, Manufacturing, Planning and Scheduling, Order Entry, Finance, the plant floor and others.

2) Part numbers are unique. If an existing item is revised, and the new item is different in form, fit or function from the old item, a new part number is required. Simply changing revision letters on a drawing and not assigning a new part number is not adequate.

3) Bills of material are made of part numbers, not drawing numbers. Part numbers identify parts; drawing numbers identify drawings. Although the same digits may be used to identify the engineering drawing and the part, the digits are serving two different purposes.

4) The bill of material includes all items to be scheduled. This

includes subassemblies, semi-finished items and any other item necessary to schedule in the production of the finished product.

5) The bill of material contains as few levels as possible. Part numbers are not assigned and used to identify work-in-process steps. Operation numbers on the routing serve that purpose. A set of rules, agreed upon by everyone, identifies the legitimate conditions for assigning new part numbers and thus creating another level in the bill.

6) All requests to change the bill of material are approved by every customer that uses the bill before the bill is changed. Bill changes are made only after total company approval.

> In technology, simplicity is the ultimate sophistication...

Garbage In, Garbage Out

Many companies have made the costly mistake of getting computer software and immediately loading poorly structured bills into the computer files. Garbage in, garbage out. This mistake can be avoided by first explaining these basic principles to all the people in the company who use the bill of material. A lot of education to get a common understanding is the best preventive medicine.

Granted, it's easier to talk about restructuring the bill than it is to actually do the restructuring. The bill has probably been growing out of control for years. The typical growth is from simple to complex.

There is a saying that, In technology, simplicity is the ultimate sophistication.

There's also the confusing problem of terminology. Businesses tend to evolve their own terminology, their own language. Sometimes they forget that outsiders have to understand what's going on, and vice versa. The classic example is in the process industries, where they have "recipes" instead of "bills of material." For every term used in this book, there are probably a dozen or more terms that mean exactly the same thing in use in industry today.

The challenge is to understand and use the system, not get bogged down in semantics.

Areas within companies adopt and use their own buzz-words, adding to the Tower of Babel problem. Engineers speak engineerese. MIS people speak computerese, executives speak management-talk. According to some engineers, people on the plant floor speak in tongues. All these problems are impediments to an accurate bill, and an accurate bill is one of the first steps on the way to World Class Performance.

Discussion Points

1. Identify and discuss the different bill of material databases in your company.

2. Discuss why different departments might feel they needed their own bill of material database.

3. Discuss your company's performance problems linked to multiple bill of material databases.

4. Discuss each of the six key principles for structuring bills and identify areas, if any, where your current bill of material structuring process violates the principles.

Chapter 4

Bill Of Material Accuracy

The number one expectation of all the internal customers of the bill of material database is that the database be accurate. Stands to reason, doesn't it? If you're manufacturing bicycles and the bill of material calls for three tires per unit, you have a problem. In fact, you have a quality problem.

If we're going to meet our quality goals,then, the first thing the bill must be is accurate. By that we mean that the material on the bill is indeed the material used to build the products. No hidden corkboards in the stockroom.

What is bill of material accuracy?

Accuracy is:

1) The right part numbers listed—nothing is required but not listed or listed and not required.

2) The right quantity per unit.

3) The correct unit of measure in quantity per unit.

4) The correct structure is used.

Part numbers are often a controversial item, and we'll be dealing with them later. Right now, let's just say that each item must have a unique identifier. That part number must be correct on the bill.

How much of a certain item goes into the finished item?

If it takes ten screws to hold the cover on, and we only have seven, the product isn't going out the door. If we need six ounces of magnesium oxide to make a heating element, and the bill says six pounds, we've wasted valuable resources.

_____

Ideally, the ultimate goal is for 100 percent B/M accuracy...

_____

Just because we leave an item off the bill doesn't mean that we aren't going to use it. On a $25,000 machine, it may seem silly to include sheet metal screws that cost $10 per thousand on the bill of material. But if you *don't* include them, *someone* has to plan how and when to get those screws. They won't appear by magic. By not including them on the bill of material, you've just passed the responsibility for scheduling the parts to another party and an informal system. One company we visited had a unique way of maintaining inventory. There were two lines drawn on the stockroom wall. When the parts got below the bottom line, enough were ordered to reach the top line. No problem, unless there were changes in the number of products made and no one repainted the line—then we're talking chaos.

Kanban (or demand pull) is an effective tool in some cases to order material. Does it eliminate the need for an accurate and complete bill? Emphatically not. We still must determine the inventory level to trigger the Kanban replenishment. Trial and error—if we run out, raise the Kanban level—leaves too much room for the second part of the phrase—error. The bill is needed to calculate the material requirements and set the Kanban level.

The parent/component relationship must be correct. We need to know which items go into which intermediates, semi-finished items, subassemblies or finished products.

Ideally, the ultimate goal is for the bill to be 100 percent accurate. Any lesser goal violates the key principle of TQM.

The m*inimum* bill of material accuracy is 98 percent; that is,

98 percent of the bills of material contain no errors in either components, quantities per assembly or structure (in measuring B/M accuracy, we're evaluating each single-level bill).

This usually gets a groan in the Bill of Material class. But this is very real and very reachable goal. The companies mentioned in this book—Centrilift, Bently Nevada, APCOM, Connaught Labs, Cooper Canada and Blue Bird have achieved a 98 percent bill of material accuracy, and, in fact, have exceeded 98 percent in many products.

The 98 percent figure sometimes causes people to stumble. Don't be in awe of the 98 percent figure. Go for continuous improvement. Suppose you check one of your company's bills of material and you discover that it's 40 percent accurate—the real bill of material is written on a chalkboard in the men's room. If the bill of material accuracy rises from 40 percent to 75 percent, and the chalkboard in the men's room is taken down, your company has already benefited tremendously. Choking on the 98 percent figure and then doing nothing accomplishes nothing.

Techniques To Measure Accuracy

Accuracy means the percentage of single level bills that conformed 100 percent to the four expectations we cited earlier. For example, if one product consisted of one single level bill with 100 components and one component was wrong, the accuracy is zero. Consider another product with nine components and each of them has ten components, a total of ten single level bills and 100 items. If one of the components is wrong the bill accuracy is 90 percent. Obviously, as we flatten the bills, eliminating unnecessary levels, it becomes more difficult to reach 100 percent accuracy.

There are several methods for checking bill of material accuracy. Here are six approaches to check accuracy:

1. Review a sample bill of material. Have a group of three or four people review a sample set of bills; ideally, the computer printout from the company database. Select one person who designs, another who plans and a third who manufacturers the product. Ask them to bring to the meeting any information they have about the bill. Put them in a conference room and let them look at each bill. If they can't agree, it's probably not an accurate bill. This should be an on-going process, even if you're at 98 percent accuracy. Just because you get to 98 percent doesn't mean you're going to stay there forever. It's a good idea to have a monthly audit team constantly checking individual, single-level bills to maintain accuracy.

2. Pick and issue the parts according to the bill. Are these the parts necessary to build the product? Can you build the product with these parts? Again, be reasonable. If your product is large and complicated, work your way through subassemblies. Keep track of the number of orders issued with errors, and pay attention to feedback from the plant floor.

3. Monitor any unplanned issues or receipts from and to the stockroom. When extra parts are requisitioned from the stockroom, or parts are returned to the stockroom, it can indicate a bill of material problem. Check this carefully, though, since excess issues and receipts can also be a sign of scrap or rework on the line.

4. Watch for production line excesses. Do parts stack up at one work station? A large pile of parts around one machine is a good indication that more are being issued than are needed.

5. Break a product or component down and check the parts (or the solution in chemical products) against the bill of material. Obviously, common sense applies here as well—you're not going to get to disassemble a whole B-1 bomber. You can, though, disassemble a subassembly of even the biggest product.

6. Do a cost roll-up using the bill, then compare it to the real cost of producing the item. Large dollar discrepancies signify a potential error in the bill.

Checking B/M accuracy is not going to be an overnight project. It will probably require three to six months of concentrated effort to just get a handle on what the accuracy is and to identify the common causes of error. It may take an additional three to six months—or more—to get the bills to 98 percent accuracy. The goal is 100 percent accuracy. And just because a bill is accurate doesn't mean it will stay accurate. An on-going audit is essential.

Cleaning up the bill of material may seem like an over-whelming project. A lot of effort, yes. Impossible, no. Use the standard problem-solving tools normally associated with TQM, including measuring, charting, root cause analysis, fishbone diagrams, pareto and the like. The task of cleaning up the bills is an excellent place to apply these tools and make the problem-solving training relevant. Make your bill of material effort part of your total quality program. It should also show you that cleaning up the bill is another one of those functions that belongs to human beings, not machines.

"It's like the example of the guy who plays golf," says Dave Biggs of Bently Nevada. "It shouldn't take you too long to figure out that the skill of the game is not in the clubs, but in the hands of the golfer...When we first started cleaning up our bill situation, we worried about the `clubs' for a long time—the technology, the computers, the software. We fortunately realized pretty quickly that the high-tech stuff wasn't that important. I don't know what our `handicap' is now, but it can still be improved..."

Over Or Under Structured?

It's impossible just to look at a bill structure and say whether it is overstructured or understructured. It takes some serious analysis of the bill and your own manufacturing processes.

The only legitimate reason for having more than two levels in the bill is planning and scheduling.

What does that mean?

The simplest bill of material is two levels: Raw materials and finished product.

There are many reasons—some legitimate, some not—for levels in the bill. Additional levels in the bill of material may be added to document what is happening in the manufacturing process, such as the creation of a subassembly or intermediates that will be inventoried. In too many cases, levels in the bill were used as a substitute for operational steps best identified in the routing—when a product went to a different work station, it was assigned a different number, which created another level in the bill. The bill was also used for accumulating labor costs, to track scrap and WIP. In other cases, levels in the bill were created to find a home for drawing numbers.

The number of levels in the bill should be minimized. Each level in the bill creates extra paperwork, extends the lead time and increases the work necessary to maintain the bill.

Other Items To Include On The Bill

As long as we're starting fights in bars, let's look at another controversial area. That is using the bill of material to schedule non-product-related items.

> What we're trying to do here is minimize surprises...

That includes items such as drawings, tooling, routings and special supplies to manufacture the product.

Why would we want to include these items on the bill of material?

Well, consider this story. A company we consulted with manufactured large electric generators. After restructuring, its bill of material was in pretty good shape. It made, however, the decision not to put the company decal, which was affixed to each generator, on the bill. The reasons the company had were good ones, too. The company that manufactured the decals was just down the street from the main plant. The decals, which cost only a few cents apiece, could be produced quickly. It didn't seem worth the effort to add them to the bill, then plan and schedule decals. As it happened, the end of the fiscal year fell on a Friday, and the plant was pushing to ship a lot of material out before midnight. There were $1,250,000 worth of generators sitting on the loading dock waiting Friday afternoon for decals when the final assemblers ran out. A quick call to the decal manufacturer bought a positive response—"No problem," they said. "We'll set up and get them to you first thing Monday morning..."

You can bet that now the decals are on the bill of material and are planned and scheduled.

A lot of what we're trying to do here is minimize surprises. No person can spend too long in manufacturing without coming away with a healthy respect for Murphy's Law. A manufacturing plant can be an amazingly complicated and complex place. Production machines, people, computers and paperwork all have to come together and function for the system to work.

The question is how can we use the bill of material to make that whole system more efficient? We can do that by including non-product-related items on the bill.

The plant floor may require Engineering Specifications, drawings, patterns, etc., for reference. Putting them on the bill guarantees (or should guarantee) that the plant floor will have the information it needs to build the product.

> After all, the bill of material is company information...

Tooling is another touchy point. In many manufacturing processes, tooling must be constantly replaced or repaired. An example would be drill bits that wear down or even electronic test equipment that requires regular calibration testing. Time and replacement parts for tooling must be built into the schedule to keep the system functioning smoothly. Tool replacements can be built into the bill of material and planned and scheduled just as easily as any other component. The recalibrating can be built into the bill.

We often overlook special supplies as items that can bring the system to a standstill. An example here might be rubber gloves for workers in a chemical plant, or white cotton gloves for workers handling metal that might tarnish. The cotton gloves are a good example. A company that manufactures copper cups needed those gloves, which, like the decals, only cost a fraction of a cent apiece, but they were necessary to the production process. *Someone* has to plan and schedule those gloves. It should be a part of the formal system.

The bill of material is indeed company information. Its uses run through the entire company, and its accuracy is absolutely necessary. It can be used to ease some of the rough spots in the manufacturing process but only to the extent that we're willing to use it. Like any tool, the real utility of the bill of material is dependent on the people who use it. That's a point you'll be reading again and again in this book—in the pursuit of World Class, people are the important part.

Discussion Points

1. Discuss who is the most demanding "customer" of your company bill of material and why. What are their requirements?

2. Discuss the definition of an accurate bill of material. Identify appropriate ways to measure the accuracy of your bills.

3. Do you measure the bill of material accuracy now? How is the accuracy measured, and by whom?

4. How do additional levels in the bill of material impact quality, cost and speed in your business?

5. What are the reasons for having more than two levels in the bill of material in your business?

6. Discuss the use of part numbers, drawing or specification numbers and bills of material in your business.

7. Discuss a situation where a drawing or schematic diagram may be required, but a corresponding part number is not necessary.

8. Discuss items that are not included on your bill of material currently, but should be added.

9. Discuss the linkage of improving bill of material structure and accuracy with your Total Quality Management efforts.

Chapter 5

The Payoff

Strange as it may sound, the bill of material is the Achilles heel of making our factories more competitive. Many American industries grew up in relatively easy times. For years such American industries as steel, automobiles, computers and electronics were the only game in town, juggling market share among major American players and turning a blind eye toward the rest of the world.

The classic example is the automobile industry, virtually oblivious to foreign imports until jarred by a gas crisis, but other examples are laced through the last 20 years of manufacturing history. Xerox and IBM fighting it out for the office copier market while ignoring the Japanese. The American consumer electronics industry. Textiles. Chemicals. The list goes on and on.

When we didn't face international competition, we could afford to run our industries sloppily. If we own the marketplace, we can manufacture any way we want and still make money. Old Joe's little black book was all the bill of material we needed. Those days are past us now. We used to think in terms of the "domestic" and the "foreign" markets (actually, we used to think in terms of the "local," "domestic" and "foreign" markets). Now, those ideas seem hopelessly provincial. There is only one market, and it encompasses the globe.

The way we stay alive in a tough world market is through manufacturing excellence, continuous improvement in all aspects of the manufacturing environment. You might define manufacturing excellence as, "Doing it right the first time." There's a lot to be said for the old cliché about there never being enough time to do it right the first time, but always enough time to do it over.

The business processes—and the bill of material is one of them—must be, to borrow a buzzword, re-engineered to be faster and less costly. This means making tasks that are presently necessary unnecessary, then eliminating them. This means change.

The Meaning Of Excellence

Manufacturing excellence means increases in quality and service, intelligent planning and managing of the resources. Manufacturing excellence means one set of numbers that the whole company uses. That's where a revamped, accurate, correctly structured bill of material comes in. A correctly structured bill is an important first step in pursuing World Class Performance.

Reaching those goals, however, is going to require some behavior modification.

I recall one company where the engineers agreed to go to a company database but insisted on keeping their engineering bills "just in case." The company president wisely agreed, allowing them to keep the engineering bills in sealed boxes in Engineering. Eventually, the engineers tossed the boxes out on their own. Why? Because it had been demonstrated to their satisfaction that the system *worked*.

Let's take a look at some of the companies who faced a bill restructuring and not only survived, but prospered.

Bently Nevada in Minden, Nevada, began life as Bently Scientific, a one-man operation founded by Don Bently to build scientific test equipment. The company now employs more than 1500 engineers, technicians, manufacturing and sales personnel around the world, the leader in manufacturing rotating machinery monitoring and information systems.

Bently suffered from a common manufacturing disease of the 1960s and early 1970s—the company's growth outstripped its management systems.

The bill of material was thumbtacked to a wall, and it was only the presence of many long-time employees who knew how the products were built that kept anything at all going out the back door. New product introduction was an agonizing procedure, with one memorable product requiring more than 1,000 engineering change orders before it got off the ground. Just when it seemed as if things could get no worse, Bently Nevada suffered a major fire.

> Reaching these goals is going to require some behavior modification...

"We were in a survival mode after the fire," says Dave Biggs, vice president. "Basically, through necessity, we threw out the motherhood and apple pie statements and got down to what we really needed to do to survive in this business."

With the informal system in shambles, Bently Nevada began implementing MRP II. Over a grueling several-year period, Bently Nevada began getting the business under control. Revamping the bill of material was central to that control—the company had to know how to build the products it sold.

"And the bill was all tied up with order entry and manufacturing," says Biggs. "With some of our older products, it was easier to build them than it was to order them. After the fire, we sat down and really thought out the question of how we could drive the manufacturing organization so we could build what we sold."

The Big Payoff

The result?

The cost of quality went down—big time!

After restructuring the bill of material, a 50 percent reduction of the overhead cost of processing the customer order.

"We used to have 12 customer service people downstairs doing nothing but figuring out what people had ordered," Biggs says. "Now we have six. We've also made it easier for the customer to order, and we're working on making it even easier."

One of the first things Bently Nevada did was bring representatives from all areas of the company in and sit them in a room with a huge blackboard.

> "We didn't have one database, we had five or six..."

"We walked through the logic of our software programs and the kind of bill we wanted," Dave Biggs says, "trying to determine if we drive at this level, what comes out the bottom. What are we going to end up buying, and what are we going to end up building? Everybody should go through this process. No one should just walk in, take a bill of material processor or whatever software program they're using and just trust in God that whatever goes in the top comes out the bottom in the correct numbers."

Bently Nevada began MRP II with about 300 people in manufacturing and $17 million in business. There are now almost 900 people in manufacturing worldwide and more than $150 million in business.

"It's a major difference," says the Vice President of Manufacturing. "We didn't have one database. We had five or six. We had one in Marketing; we had one in Sales; we had a catalog; we had engineering documentation; we had the configuration file and, finally, we had what people were really building. Millions of pieces of paper. Now we have a database, and it's in the computer."

The Big Yellow Bus Dilemma

Blue Bird's product is one of the most familiar products in America—the big yellow school bus. Blue Bird's been manufacturing those yellow buses in the same Georgia town since 1927. Things were actually going well at Blue Bird when, in the early

1970s, the company took a new look at how the business was run. One consultant's comment was that he'd never seen such a large warehouse with an assembly line running through it.

An assembly line for a bus has to be huge, and Blue Bird didn't just build a bus. It built hundreds, thousands of *different* buses, sensitive to legal requirements in thousands of school districts. In addition, Blue Bird supplied buses for numerous other applications, from prison system convict carriers to luxury ultra-expensive motorhomes. The way Blue Bird coped with this problem was inventory, inventory and more inventory.

After all, they reasoned, if we don't know exactly what we're going to build, we'd better get a whole bunch of everything to be ready.

There were two "official" bills of material, but the real bills were in the heads of workers on the shop floor.

"We knew the bills had to get accurate," says Ray Dollar of Blue Bird.

Easier said than done. Blue Bird offered some 900 basic body plans, with many additional options for each body plan, pushing the number of unique buses into the stratosphere. Each bus consisted of between 1,800 and 3,000 parts.

"There's no such thing as an average or standard bus," says Dollar.

"We worked on what hurt the most," says Vernon Wright, in charge of master scheduling at Blue Bird. "We had a `boneyard' with buses waiting for parts—entrance doors, windows, seats, all sorts of parts. Overtime was a big problem as we all scrambled to meet the delivery dates."

Blue Bird still has a boneyard, but now there are rarely more than four buses in it. Instead of inventory, inventory, inventory, some portions of the line run with no safety stock at all. Back in the 1970s, it took as many as 4,000 man-hours just to take the annual physical inventory. Ten years later, it's 860 man-hours. Inventory accuracy went from 71 percent to 99.94 percent.

Blue Bird's advertising campaign in the trade publications reflects its new-found strength:

"Delivery dates you can count on," reads one ad. "98 percent right and not yet satisfied..."

A modularized bill coupled with a planning bill based on forecasts that can be trusted has produced tremendous results. Blue Bird is a fierce competitor (we still haven't seen any Japanese school buses), and it has turned seasonal employment for many workers into a full-time, 12-month-a-year job.

"Our modularized bill gives us flexibility," says Wright.

Getting Out Of Hot Water

Talk about seasonal industries, APCOM's water heater heating elements are right up there with Christmas trees. Every November, APCOM's customers start ordering heating elements. Throughout the winter the order numbers increase. Then, in spring, the orders diminish, until, by April, there were few orders to keep the plant going.

A 50 to 60 percent increase in seasonal materials was normal.

To help facilitate production and accounting, APCOM had invested in a computer system. Unfortunately, the computer system was as much a part of the problem as the solution.

While the company was investigating a new hardware system to replace APCOM's bug-ridden disaster, it also began investigating business management systems.

APCOM's largest customer is their parent company. The advantage is a guaranteed market; the disadvantage is a customer who demands product immediately—daily production changes.

During the busy season daily production meetings were held with two functions—launch and expedite.

There were no analyses or plans; the only management tool was the sales order. Lead time to manufacture was a fairly long six to eight weeks, and the customer demanded delivery in days. APCOM's response was to fill up the warehouse with raw materials—all kinds of materials, since no one was sure what the orders were going to be.

Everything was short-term, survival mode.

After a year of start and stop, APCOM hammered out a new bill of material structure. That structure, though, while textbook-perfect, did not reflect the way the product was made. The new bill of material had several sublevels, each subassembly with a different part number, requiring lots of extra paperwork. In reality, the heating units flowed through the line, from beginning to end.

"We didn't know where we were going with the bill," members of the Project Team lamented. "There was a logical, rational reason for us structuring the bill the way we did. It just didn't have anything to do with the real world."

> "Everything was short-term, survival mode..."

In the face of a shop floor rebellion, APCOM went back to the drawing board again.

The result was a bill of material system utilizing backflushing as a technique for minimum transactions to maintain accurate inventory records. The modularized bill, along with other techniques, led to an over 50 percent reduction in inventory.

Bills of material are audited every week. A 98 percent accuracy standard has become a way of life, with 27 weeks at 100 percent now being the goal to beat. Forecasting and a well-designed planning bill has helped level out the seasonal fluctuations.

APCOM has managed to get in a position where it doesn't have to make any giant steps to up production. The payoff has been a stable workload and work force.

Surviving The Bust

"It has been," says Jerry Hastings, vice president of Centrilift, "an interesting couple of years." That's similar to the Chinese curse of living in interesting times.

Centrilift manufactures pumps that are used in oil wells to bring oil to the surface. For the last couple of years, decreasing oil prices worldwide have put the hammerlock on industries like Centrilift, turning much of Oklahoma, where Centrilift is located, into an area of high unemployment and failed businesses.

For Centrilift, success is defined as survival.

Part of that recipe for survival includes a series of innovative ideas, using American systems, Japanese ideas and just plain old common sense to keep a multi-million dollar business afloat in hard times.

Originally, Centrilift decided to implement MRP II as part of a plan to deal with the boom times of the 1970s. In 1980 the company relocated, carrying very few people from the old location to the new location. One of the advantages was that the new employees, right down to the hourly floor workers, were educated early on about the importance of an accurate bill of material.

"I think that was really an asset," says Dale Hendrix, materials manager. "I put in 20 years at a company where we were sort of *embedded* with the product. We knew the product and every part number by heart. We didn't need a bill of material, because we all knew how to build the stuff."

The first thing management did was bring all areas of the company into the discussion of the bill. When hostilities broke out—and they do break out—the problem areas were discussed until a decision was reached. The most important point in the education process was that everyone understand the logic of the new bills, because once they had the logic down, the rest would come easy.

"There is always an old guard who is quick to point out when you screw up," says Hendrix. "But our inventory has dropped $10,000,000 in the last nine months. It only dropped because we got those bills where we could manage a planning system that *worked*...And without the proper bill of material logic to start with, we'd never have been able to structure our bills the way we did."

The structuring of the bill has paid such big dividends, he adds, that if a bill of material election was held at Centrilift today, 98 percent of the people there would vote in favor of the present structure. While they're waiting for better times, Centrilift is still producing.

Four different companies with four different sets of problems. Yet each company found ways to cope with those problems. And for each company, those problem-solving methods centered around the bill of material. The creation of a company database is cited as one of the most important steps in controlling the business.

Discussion Points

1. Discuss some specific current problems cause by poor bill of material quality.

2. Estimate the cost of poor quality bills of material.

3. Identify some specific opportunities for making quality improvements in your bills of material.

Restructuring The Bill of Material

In the previous chapters we've been looking at the bill of material from a general viewpoint, pointing out problem areas, establishing accuracy checks and seeing how the bill of material fits into the overall plan of a company.

For the next few chapters we'll be dealing with the nuts and bolts of restructuring the bill. The need to sell the necessity of running the business better, of eliminating all unnecessary activities, has passed. We now need to move to restructuring the bill of material to meet the needs of the most demanding customer, the planning and scheduling system.

Once you've made the decision to create a company database, you'll need to answer some practical questions to make those changes happen. Some of the basic questions are:

1) What do all these strange terms like phantom, modularizing and planning bills mean, exactly? Sometimes it seems like half the battle is in communication. We learned very early on in the consulting business that it was vitally important to define terms, even terms that "everyone" knows.

2) When and how should part numbers be assigned? Do special parts get a number? Should the part numbers be significant or non-significant? Here's another good topic for starting fights in bars.

3) What should be included on or excluded from the bill of material? One company agonized over white rats...

4) How are one-time substitutions and customer requests for special products to be handled? The customer is always right, and sometimes his or her being right has significant impact on the manufacturing process.

5) Our company has millions of end items. Do we need to structure a million bills of material to handle all those end items? How do we cope with multiple end items and options?

6) What's the best way to deal with engineering changes? Is there a way to use already existing planning methods to smooth the introduction of new products?

> A lot of companies agree with the idea of a company database, but haven't taken any steps to make that database a reality...

7) Is there a single correct way to structure the bill, or does the structure change when the manufacturing process changes?

All these questions will be answered in the following section.

A lot of people agree philosophically with the idea of a single company database, but they haven't taken any steps to make that a reality in their own company. The typical reason we hear is that those people don't have the answers to the basic questions we listed above, and they can't imagine how such a system can work.

In fact, we've heard the same excuses so many times that we've constructed a Filibuster Kit, guaranteed to delay meaningful progress on bill restructuring for at least a couple of years. There are just a few basic issues, but they can be debated endlessly:

• Whether the part numbers should be significant or not.

• Whether to put small parts or inexpensive items such as nuts and bolts on the bill of material.

- Whether Engineering and Manufacturing need a separate bill of material.
- Whether or not we should keep the bill on the drawing, process sheet or specification documentation.
- And the ever-popular debate over who gets stuck with the job of restructuring the bill.

While we're using our Filibuster Kit to its fullest, we're overlooking such problems as overstructured bills, understructured and incomplete bills, chaotic engineering changes and poor handling of options and specials.

We've shown you in the preceding chapters not only how a properly constructed single bill system can work, but the way it is working at a number of companies.

Now that you know the goals, let's look at the tools to achieve those goals.

Chapter 6

Revising the Bill of Material

Remember: *In technology, simplicity is the ultimate sophistication.*

As we look at restructuring the bill of material, we need to keep in mind the idea of moving from the complex to the simple. We want to move toward a bill of material structure that will serve as a company database, that will serve the needs of all the internal customers. In the past we've done that by getting larger, moving from simple to complex. Going from a small parts list to an add-delete bill, hanging optional features on the original structure.

What we really need to do is step back and analyze what function the bill needs to serve. Architect Frank Lloyd Wright wrote that "form follows function." The final form or structure of the bill is a reflection of what we want the bill to do.

The bill also needs to be an accurate reflection of the way we really make the product, which is another way of saying the bill can't be structured in a vacuum. There are ample examples of good companies first structuring the bill, then trying to force the manufacturing processes into that structure. At APCOM, the shop floor foremen flatly refused to go along with the new system, because they knew that the new bill didn't mirror the way they manufactured the product. Other companies have agonized over modularizing their bills when they, in fact, have only a few end items and no options.

> Each bill is tailored for the company using it, but structured using proven methods and techniques...

The bill of material structuring process needs to be tailored for the company using it, but those bills can be structured using proven methods and techniques. The next chapters will outline those techniques.

We also want to get people from the plant floor, people who build the product, involved early on to make sure the bill accurately reflects the way the product is *really* manufactured.

First, we'll be looking at the "end-item mentality." One of the first barriers we run into in restructuring the bill of material is the way we look at the product. After years of teaching Bill of Material classes, we've come to the conclusion that people are in love with their product. As well they should be! The product is what makes them money, why they got into the business in the first place. Traditionally, we've structured the bill of material around the end item, and that isn't always the best way.

Next, we'll be defining terms. Terms such as part numbers, routings and engineering drawings are subject to a surprising number of misinterpretations. Terms have a way of becoming industry-specific or even company-specific. A quick example is a company that insists it has no bill of material, but uses a recipe to determine what goes into a product. Semantic confusion has put the skids to more than one bill of material revamping, yet that confusion is easy to clear up.

A Little Controversy

We'll also be looking at two controversial subjects, part numbers and product engineering documentation (drawings, test specs, QA specs, finishing specs). When and how should part numbers be assigned? When should they be changed? Should part numbers be significant, that is, should they be more than simply an identifier? Every company is sure it's discovered the secret to the perfect part number, the revealed truth about how to assign numbers to parts.

Engineering drawings are a similar hot topic. As a carryover from precomputer days, the bill of material often ended up in the upper right-hand corner of the engineering drawing. (Countless generations of drafting students were taught that was where the bill belonged.) With the rise of computer-assisted drawing and design (CAD), the bill on the drawing has gotten a "new lease on life," since the computer drawings are so much easier to reproduce. Is that, though, where the bill should go? We think not, and we'll outline some strategies for getting the bill off the drawings. We'll also look at methods to make the drawings more useful, and how to guarantee the drawings will be available when and where we need them.

Traditionally, process industries have seen themselves as facing different problems than other types of industries. As opposed to job shops and build- or assemble-to-order industries, process industries have more of a flow, product constantly flowing through the processes. An examination of the facts, though, leads to the conclusion that while there might be different emphasis, the problems process industries face are the same as those facing other industries, and the same solutions can be adopted.

The basic planning for revamping the bill includes a critical view of the production methods. How do we make the product, and how should that be reflected in the bill?

On Or Off?

We also delve into another controversial area, that of what to include on and exclude from the bill of material. When we reach this point in class, we invariably have one (or more) person who says something to the effect that, "You're not telling me that we should include `little bitty screws' on the bill of material, are you?" That's exactly what we're saying. Just because you choose to exclude an item from the bill of material doesn't mean that someone has to plan and schedule the item. It may be the stock boy, who runs down to the hardware store every so often to pick up some sandpaper that's infrequently used in a process. It may be

> "You aren't suggesting we include 'little bitty' screws on the bill of material, are you?"

a line foreman, who knows that, once a month, someone has to order another 10,000 6/32 screws. By choosing to place an item on the bill instead of leaving it off, you're signaling that the item will be planned and scheduled using the formal system instead of trusting luck and the informal system to get what you need when you need it.

In upcoming chapters, we'll be dealing with such topics as bill structuring, modularizing, changing and the introduction of new products.

In dealing with bills, we say that, "Shallower is better." A bill that has the fewest possible levels is easier to maintain and results in less paperwork. Too often, we include levels in the bill for such reasons as labor collection or work-in-process inventory value or to gather work at a particular workstation, functions that are better served by using the routing. The only legitimate reason for a level in the bill of material is planning and scheduling.

One of the tools we use in restructuring a bill is the phantom, also known as a pseudo or blow-through. The phantom is a grouping of parts that may or may not be able to be assembled, used strictly as a convenience in planning and scheduling. Phantoms have numerous uses, but one of their main uses is in helping to cope with products that are offered with many customer-specified options.

When there are only two or three end items manufactured by a company, the bill of material process is easier than that of a company with many end items created by combining several options. In fact, a company with relatively few options can end up with thousands of end items. We could assign each of those end items a part number and create a separate bill of material for each end item. Modern computers can handle that, to be sure, and deciding to handle the situation that way will make your computer software vendor very happy. The problems, though, come in predicting when and which items should be run and in maintaining the many bills.

Modularizing The Bill

A better way of dealing with options and multiple end items is through *modularizing* the bill of material. Modularizing the bill means grouping parts in a product by the option they're sensitive to. A 220-volt test instrument, for example, requires a different transformer than a 110-volt unit. The transformer, then, is sensitive to the voltage option.

By creating bills for each option, not each end item, we have the advantages of fewer bills of material, less bill of material maintenance, more efficient order entry—an increasingly critical area as products become more complex—and easier forecasting of options.

After modularizing the bill, we create a planning bill, which is basically a sorting of the Master Bill of Material for planning and forecasting purposes. Using historical information and marketing forecasts, we figure the percentage of the total sales each option will require. We can then plan and schedule accordingly.

The modularized bill does allow for much more efficient order entry. The bill can be configured at customer order entry time in such a way as to *create* the unique bill of material for each customer order. Some companies use a computerized "configurator" system to help speed up this critical order entry time.

Another important tool in bill of material restructuring is the requirements file, a computer file that allows you to tie a bill of material to a specific order. This allows for lot traceability, efficient one-time substitutions and lead time offsets.

Challenging Changes

One of the toughest areas to get a handle on has been changes to the bill of material. With a carefully structured bill and the right tools and procedures in place, changes can be relatively painless. For a start, every company needs a bill of material change policy, outlining why and how the bill can be changed. Each change—and suggestions for changes can come from all areas of the company, not just Engineering—needs to be speedily reviewed and a decision made on accepting or rejecting the change.

The change policy can also be used to set guidelines for the phase out of old parts and the phase in of new parts.

> By carefully following proven techniques, you avoid the costly grief of restructuring a newly restructured bill..."

We also show how to develop a formal policy for the introduction of new products, an area that often, in the words of one engineer, "resembles a cross between a Chinese fire drill and World War III." We provide for a period of research and development with minimal paperwork for changes, then bring the new product rapidly into the formal system. By constantly monitoring the introduction, we avoid the worst of the problems that typically plague such events.

The result is that the restructuring of the bill of material, with its advantages to our company, is completed with a minimum of grief and pain. After we create a single company database, we can be sure of the bill accuracy, sure that everyone is working from the same information, sure that the product is being built as it was designed, sure that the right materials are being ordered to be available at the right times and sure that production cost calculations are based on parts really used to build the product.

Restructuring a bill of material can be a costly and time-consuming task. It's nitty-gritty work. Doing it the first time is tough enough. Follow the strategies we've outlined in the following chapters and use the tools given, and you won't have to worry about the added grief of restructuring a restructured bill!

Discussion Points

1. Seven frequently asked questions are listed in the introduction to Section II. Discuss which of those questions are the most relevant to your business.

2. The Filibuster Kit listed in the introduction to this section includes five items. Which ones apply to your business?

3. Modularizing bills of material, using phantoms, managing bill of material changes, adding necessary or deleting unnecessary levels and raising the accuracy of bills of material are separate and distinct issues. Briefly discuss what each of these issues means and which ones are *potentially* applicable to your business.

Chapter 7

Speaking English— Defining Terms

We've mentioned earlier the Tower of Babel syndrome— different industries, different companies, sometimes different areas of the same company speaking different "languages." I see this practically every time I speak before any professional group. During or after the presentation someone will invariably ask what I meant by...

It's almost impossible to accomplish a task such as restructuring the bill of material when everyone is not speaking the same language. Therefore, defining terms is critical.

Let's look at some of the terms that might cause confusion when discussing our company's bill of material database:

Bill of Material
Part Number
Routing
Engineering Drawing (or Specification Sheet)
Parts List

Take a look at the graphic on the next page. You can see that within the bill of material database, there are the item master file,

Typical B/M Data Base Files

Figure 1: The Bill of Material Database Files

the bill of material file, the routing file, the requirements file and, in some companies, CAD/CAM file.

We'll look at these and other terms and do our best to see that we're all talking the same language.

Bill of Material

Bill of Material: The bill of material is a list of item numbers needed to make the parent item. That includes the obvious items, such as component parts, items or raw materials. It also includes any subassemblies, intermediates and semi-finished items, or any *phantoms* or *pseudos*—in essence, dummy part numbers created to facilitate planning—any non-component item necessary for the production of the parent.

The bill of material masquerades under a number of different names. In the process industries, it might be called the recipe or the formula. Some industries refer to the bill of material as the specification or specs, a holdover from the earlier term of engineering specifications. As we mentioned earlier, every industry must have a bill of material. It may exist only in the shop foreman's head or written in Magic Marker on the warehouse wall.

You can't make a product without knowing what goes into it.

Part Numbers

Part Numbers: Here's a tricky one and a whole other bag of worms, which we'll attempt to decipher here. A part number is a unique identifier, a numeric or alphanumeric grouping that identifies one and only one object.

Take a box of five crayons—red, yellow, blue, green, black. If it matters what color those crayons are, obviously they each must have a different part number. If, on the other hand, you work in a wax retrieval company, if there is any such thing, and color doesn't matter, you can assign all "scrap" crayons the same part number.

There is no shortage of part numbers!

As self-evident as that seems, assigning part numbers is one of the first stumbling blocks to an accurate bill of material. The "what-ifs" run something along the line of, "It's a one-time replacement part or it's almost the same, so why should we go through the expense and grief of assigning a new part number to it?" If the part can be used as a replacement *in every instance*, possibly a new part number isn't necessary. Yet, consider the future. Is there an assembly or a parent where the substitute part can be used and the original couldn't? If you can think of such a situation, however farfetched, it's likely that Murphy's Law will catch up with you, probably next week. In this case, a new part number is needed.

Too many companies treat part numbers as if there were a very finite number in the universe, and every one they pass out means there's one less to use. There seems to be a Conservation of Part Numbers Law in engineering schools. I visited one company and was surprised at how few items were on the bill of material. When I asked the product engineer about the bill, he just laughed. Those weren't the only items necessary to build the product, he said.

What wasn't on the bill, I asked.

Special parts.

Why weren't they on the bill?

The engineer was shocked. You're not suggesting we put the special parts on the bill, he said, and *waste* a part number!

It is safer to err in favor of assigning a new part number rather than figure out your way around having not assigned one.

These are the basic "ground rules" for assigning part numbers:

1) Every item, purchased or manufactured, that has to be scheduled to satisfy forecast or special order requirements should have a part number and be included in the bill of material. Semi-finished materials, subassemblies, intermediates used in chemical manufacturing and manufacturing subassemblies are all included.

2) When a part is sold for service or replacement, a part number must be assigned, even if it is not manufactured and issued from inventory when the end item is produced.

3) It is sometimes necessary to assign a part number to a transient subassembly (process industries often call these transient items intermediates). A subassembly that is assembled on a feeder assembly line and consumed within a few minutes or hours in final assembly is an example of a transient subassembly. When an imbalance in inventory due to overruns or quality rejections occurs on mating parts, a few of the transient subassemblies may be left in the feeder assembly area at the end of a final assembly run. If a transient subassembly is frequently returned to stock, a part number must be assigned and a corresponding bill of material created. This is one of the functions of a *phantom*. By making the lead time zero and making the phantom lot-for-lot order quantity, MRP will consume any inventory that exists, but "blow-through" to the next level of the bill if no inventory exists. We'll have a more thorough discussion of phantoms later.

Hopefully, these conditions will be minimized by keeping lot sizes small, using pull systems and going, where possible, to more continuous, repetitive manufacturing.

4) When a customer returns a product, it is disassembled and a subassembly is returned to the stockroom, another legitimate condition exists for inserting an additional level in the bill of material. A part number must be assigned to the subassembly to account for the inventory and consider its availability in replan-

ning future inventory requirements for its components.

In some industries, this is a major problem. Centrilift, for example, takes in pumps from the oil fields in trade. (Actually, things happen so fast in the field that there is no time for "repair," per se. As soon as a pump is pulled from a well, another pump goes in.) The old pumps are broken down for parts and stored at Centrilift satellite facilities near the oil wells. Inventory in the satellite centers fluctuates wildly as pumps are taken in and broken down for parts, rework or scrap. By assigning part numbers to salvaged items and working them into its bill, Centrilift is able to handle the large influx of salvaged parts.

5) Engineering sometimes discovers a subassembly or group of parts that are commonly used together and appear in many assemblies. This group may consist of parts used together when an option is ordered. The size of the bill of material database can be reduced with a corresponding ease of maintenance if the group of common parts are identified with a part number, even if it is not manufactured. This is a "bag of parts" concept. For example, if the same coil assembly consisting of 50 parts was used in each of 100 unique electric motors, a part number could be assigned for the coil assembly and be shown as a single item on each of the 100 bills of material for the motors. If a change were made in one of

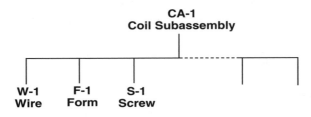

Figure 2: A coil subasembly

the common parts in the coil assembly, only one bill would need to be changed—not each of the 100 bills. If the "bag of parts" never really physically exists, the part number is coded as a phantom. If the item exists and is inventoried, it's treated like any other part number. It's not a phantom.

Significant or Non-significant?

Let's consider what kind of part numbering systems can be used. There are two: Significant and non-significant.

A significant part number is one in which the digits and/or the placement of the digits in the number carries a specific meaning. For example, it's not unusual to see a part number like 10-25-10. Suppose the item is a bolt. Maybe the first two digits identify the bolt head, the second two digits the material its made of and the third two digits the thread size. A person experienced with the numbering system could look at the number and say, "Hmmm, a hex-head stainless-steel 6/32 bolt." That's just scratching the surface, though. A *really* complex significant part number looks like this:

50-3-AB2507-1406-50-P-2100-N

Where the first two digits (50) represent the product family, the next digit (3) the material, the letters and number (AB2507) the engineering drawing number used to make the item, where used, and on and on.

Is there anything wrong with this?

Not really. It is a unique identifier, identifying one specific item.

It is, however, complicated.

Overly complicated, we'd say, and very prone to causing errors when inputting data.

Consider the chart on the following page.

The horizontal axis represents the number of digits in a part number. The vertical axis takes into account the probability of error in using that number. At about 15 digits, the probability of error hits 100 percent. Someone once asked in class whether his company should change from a 20-digit part numbering system to a 25-digit part numbering system. We said go right ahead, since the probability of error was already 100 percent. Somewhere along the line someone is going to make a mistake with 50-3-

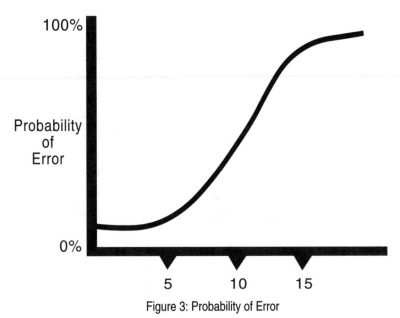

Figure 3: Probability of Error

AB2507-1406-50-P-2100-N, transpose a number or leave out a letter. The result is going to be chaos on the shop floor or a very unhappy customer. If you happen to sell $100,000 pumps that take another $100,000 to put in a very deep hole, you can't afford very many unhappy customers.

The solution to this dilemma is to use shorter *non-significant* part numbers. A non-significant part number is just a number, an identifier, telling you nothing about the item it's identifying.

Suppose we change the part number of 50-3-AB2507-1406-50-P-2100-N to 123. The likelihood of the number 123 being miscopied, misentered or otherwise incorrectly written is much, much smaller than the likelihood with 50-3-AB2507-1406-50-P-2100-N.

So why was the item assigned such a long and complex number in the first place?

In the days before computers the only practical way to communicate the heritage or information about a part number was to bury intelligence in the number with significant digits. Today's information technology offers a better alternative. The descriptive intelligence about the part number can easily be captured in the

```
             ITEM MASTER FILE
_____

BASIC:        Part Number
              Description
              Unit of Measure
              Lead Time
              P/M
              Classification Code
              Item Type/Class
              Eng. Drawing #

DYNAMIC:      On-hand Balance
              Cost
              Bin Location
_____
```

Figure 4: The Item Master Record

Item Master database. If done this way, the information is much easier to use for search and sorting. All of the disadvantages of the significant part number are avoided and none of the advantages are lost.

The killer issue with part numbers is not significant, intelligent part numbers or long or short numbers. The killer issue is not assigning unique numbers when needed.

Item Master Record

Item Master Record: The logical place to put the product information is in the item master record (also called the item record).

The item master record is the basic computer record on any item where all descriptive information about the item is stored. That record includes basic engineering information, including a description of the item, the drawing number (if the part number and the drawing number are different), the drawing size and the unit of measure and, usually, much more information. Information for manufacturing and planning is also in the item master record, including whether the item is purchased or manufactured, the lead time, the order quantity, supplier number and scrap factor. Financial information such as purchase costs and selling price is also included.

The record can also include other information such as the

corresponding supplier part numbers and other "translator" type information and, if you want, classification codes that include all the information contained in the significant part number.

The item master record can serve as a ready cross-reference between the classification codes and the part number. There is no need to carry the long, complex classification codes throughout scheduling and production, since the computer already serves a cross-referencing function anyway.

The item master record can also contain dynamic information, such as the on-hand balance, the cost and the stockroom location or locations for the part. Other information on suppliers, accounting or service parts can also be included.

We have found that part numbers of five or six digits are the most effective. They are of sufficient length to allow sufficient growth in the number of new items to be identified (a six-digit part number has a million possible combinations) while remaining short enough to minimize errors.

The significance question obviously varies from company to company. If your company has 12-digit significant numbers and 10,000 parts, it doesn't pass the sanity check to rush right out and change every number to a five-digit non-significant number. A strategy to deal with that problem, though, might include making all new parts utilize the five-digit numbers and working toward dropping the significance on the older parts. If your company has 20-digit numbers, you may be forced to go to shorter numbers to control errors.

Shorter, non-significant part numbers make it easier to get and hold bill accuracy.

Sometimes you'll have to tailor your part numbers to the special problems of your industry.

Other Potential Problems

Another potential problem area in part numbers that can be easily solved with the computer and item master record is supplier part numbers. Should you adopt the supplier part number as your own part number? The rationale for doing so is to smooth the operation between the supplier and the main company. Again, the item master record can include the supplier part number, and you can readily cross-reference between the supplier part number and your own. There's little or no advantage to adopting someone else's numbering system, which may be fraught with problems, as your own. It's hard to adapt your supplier's part numbers to your own, plus you have no control over your supplier. He may decide to change all his part numbers one afternoon, leaving you in the lurch. Plus, you may switch to a different supplier and want to avoid changing all your documentation. Stick to your own part numbers.

Part Numbers And Drawing Numbers

> If the drawing number and the part number are the same, you run into many new problems...

Another question is whether the part number should be the same as the drawing number. (In the process industries, instead of drawing numbers, there are process sheets, specification documents and similar documentation. They still face the same problems.) The thing to keep in mind here is that the part number and the drawing number serve different purposes. The part number is the unique identifier of the item, while the drawing number leads you to the visual aid for making the item. If the drawing number and the part number are the same, you run into many new problems.

The same drawing might be used for several different parts that may have the same dimension but are built of different materials. A part can be changed, requiring a new part number, without necessarily requiring a new drawing. For example, a situation where the tolerances for an item have been changed. The new tolerances make the part different, requiring a new part number. However, the drawing may only require a change in the drawing revision number, not an entirely new number.

In some cases, a part number may be required without the need for a drawing—bar stock or some other raw materials, for example. People might be confused while searching for drawings that aren't there.

If there will always be *only* one unique part or item made from each drawing, the same digits can be used to identify both. When the variations from the same basic drawing start to evolve, the problems begin. Many times companies try to use the drawing number as the base number and affix a dash number as a suffix to create the part number. Although the hybrid approach can be made to work, it's unwieldy and we don't recommend it.

There's no reason to go looking for trouble. Try to keep the part numbers and the drawing numbers separate, and potential problems are avoided.

Again, any subassembly that is stocked should have its own part number. Phantom part numbers can be assigned to transient subassemblies and "bag of parts" type subassemblies that are not stocked.

The advantages of not having the drawing number the same as the part number include:
1) Shorter part numbers.
2) Fewer bill of material errors.
3) Less confusing; less paper-shuffling.
4) Fewer material issuing errors.
5) Fewer drawings, because one drawing number can relate to many part numbers.
6) New part numbers don't require a new drawing.

Routing

Routing: The routing is the road map showing where a manufactured part or item travels through the plant. It lists the operations for a part, the work centers where the work is done and usually identifies the amount of labor required for each operation. (See Figure 5, next page)

Manufacturing operations or steps performed on components or raw materials should be part of the routing, not the bill of material.

Operation No.	Operation Description	Work Center	Standard Time Setup	Standard Time Per Unit
10	Issue	44	--	--
20	Plating	107	1.5	.03
30	Polishing	28	.3	.10
40	Package	155	.1	.36

Figure 5: An example of a routing

Engineering Drawing

In short, there are tremendous disadvantages to having the bill of material on the engineering drawing...

Engineering Drawing: An engineering drawing is a visual aid. An engineering drawing is *not* the ideal place to document or list the bill of material. Frequently, the bill of material for an item is placed on the engineering drawing. The reason for that is twofold. First, that's the way it's *always* been done. Bills of material started out being carefully lettered on the drawing; in fact, part of the drawing. The second reason is that having the bill on the drawing is that it makes the information quickly available for reference. How can you build it if you don't know what goes in it, and how do you know what goes in it unless you have the drawing?

And that is an advantage. It may be necessary to have the bill with the drawing. But is it necessary to have the bill *on* the drawing?

Have you ever seen an engineering drawing so covered with white-out for changes that it cracked when you touched it? If the bill of material is on the drawing and there's a change in the bill, how many places must the change be made?

Right—on every drawing that includes that bill.

What do you think the likelihood of this happening is?

Moreover, the company will have to pay a draftsman to change all those bills on all those drawings. What happens when the drawing itself has to be updated?

A new wrinkle in the engineering drawing dilemma is the rise of CAD/CAM. Yes, it is easier to put a bill on each drawing with a CAD/CAM system. The problem to avoid is a separate bill in the CAD/CAM system. Some technology has the capability to update the main database from the CAD/CAM system. Others don't. The problem to avoid is maintaining two separate databases.

In short, there are tremendous disadvantages to having the bill of material on the engineering drawing. However, aside from the fact that the mere discussion of removing the bills from the drawings is enough to send some engineers into fits of frothing at the mouth, there remains the need for the information.

> Evaluate the cost-effectiveness of taking the bill off the engineering drawings and see the savings.

There's an easy way to reconcile these two positions.

The bill can be removed from the drawing and transferred, along with the appropriate find numbers (or balloon numbers or reference numbers—all three terms mean the same thing), to the bill of material file.

The bill of material can then be printed out and *stapled* or *attached* to the drawing.

Now the same drawing can be referenced for several part numbers. An example would be two subassemblies whose only difference is that one has a stainless steel component while the other has the same component, but hard chrome plated. Two part numbers are required to uniquely identify each subassembly. The same drawing can suffice for both part numbers. That also cuts down the number of drawings necessary. At Bently Nevada, special effort is taken to keep the drawings separate from the bills.

"We try to keep them as independent as possible to avoid redrawings," says a product engineer at Bently Nevada. "That's something we spent a lot of time thinking about. We didn't want a situation where any given part was referenced on any given drawing, because when you changed the part, then you had to change the drawing."

The advantages of not having the bill of material on the drawing include:

• Less time consuming and less effort to maintain B/M.
• Less costly to maintain the B/M.

Evaluate the cost-effectiveness of taking the bill off the engineering drawings and see the savings. The drawing can even be added to the bill of material and coded as a reference, guaranteeing that the proper drawing will be available at the proper time.

Of course, there are disadvantages. The biggest is that it is non-traditional, which means there's going to be a behavioral change involved. Behavioral changes are tough. We'll need cross-referencing, but that's one of the things a computer is very good at.

Parts List

Parts List: Basically, a parts list is a single level bill of material. When created in Engineering, it often does not include subassemblies or intermediates required in manufacturing. The component parts of the subassemblies are listed individually.

Discussion Points

1. Discuss the definition and use of part numbers, bills of material, routings, engineering drawings or specifications and parts lists in your business.

2. Identify any costs or time that could be saved by more clearly understanding these items.

3. If a part numbering system is an issue in your business, discuss the advantages and disadvantages of significant digits in the

part number. Discuss alternative ways the significant data currently embedded in your part number could be included in the item master record.

4. Discuss the five conditions for assigning part numbers and how these are applicable in your business. Identify examples where part numbers are currently assigned in violation of these conditions.

5. If the bill of material information is currently included on your engineering drawings or specification sheets, discuss the disadvantages. Discuss how the internal customers' requirements for this information could be met to overcome these disadvantages.

Chapter 8

Phantoms

Phantoms are one of the basic elements of restructuring a bill of material, a tool that allows us to simplify the bill. We're going to settle on the term "phantom" here, but it's frequently known as a pseudo, blow-through, transient, self-consumed, kit, module, modular bill, S-bill, partial parts list, non-stocked subassembly, convenience number and probably a few others that we've overlooked. The terminology varies from company to company and from industry to industry, so the first challenge in using phantoms is standardizing terminology.

A phantom is an item that is not normally (or maybe never) produced and put in the stockroom (i.e., inventoried).

A phantom item can:
1) Exist at any level in the bill of material.
2) Identify an item that is not usually manufactured and put into a stockroom, although the item could be.
3) Identify a group of parts that cannot possibly be assembled.
4) Identify an item that may be forecasted and master scheduled whether it's ever manufactured or not.

It is sometimes necessary to identify a group of parts that can potentially be assembled but are infrequently put into the stock-

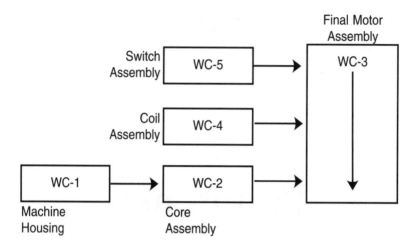

Figure 1: A series of work centers

room. These *transient subassemblies* exist for only a short period of time during the production process. For example, products such as electric motors are often put together on assembly lines. People stationed at different points on the assembly line add components or subassemblies as the product moves to their station. At the same time, other people assemble components into coil and switch subassemblies on tangent or feeder assembly lines.

The coil and switch subassemblies are quickly consumed into the final assembly. Coil and switch subassemblies aren't sent back into the stockroom, only to be withdrawn a few minutes or hours later. To do so would require a significant amount of unnecessary paperwork, inventory receipts and work orders, which does not reflect how the product is actually made.

Although these subassemblies exist for a short time, the stockroom issues components, not the coil and switch subassemblies, to make the motors. Usually, there's little reason to recognize these subassemblies; doing so would only add an extra level to the bill. There are, however, exceptions.

Residual Inventory

Sometimes there's a residual amount of coil and switch subassemblies left over after the production run. This could be the result of a scrap factor—say, several of the motor housings were unacceptable and the run was cut short by 10 percent. Or perhaps extra subassemblies were produced to compensate for the subassembly scrap factor but the extras weren't needed. We're faced with a dilemma. Should we disassemble the subassemblies and put the parts back in stock, even though we're planning a run of the same motors next week? Should we just stuff them under the assembly bench and hope the assembler remembers they're there when the next motor run comes up? (Sometimes looking under benches in factories is a like an archaeological dig in that company's product history). The best thing to do is to return the subassemblies to the stockroom and inventory them, so the next time the motors are run, the subassemblies will be used.

In order for that to happen, the subassemblies must be visible to MRP, which means that the subassemblies must be on the bill of material. We can plan to use up subassembly inventory to make motors and schedule only enough components to meet the net requirements.

This is accomplished by tagging the transient subassemblies as phantoms. The subassemblies are built, quickly consumed and not usually put into the stockroom. Most of the time, they should be ignored. It's only in the exceptional case where residual inventory exists after the production run is completed that they need to be recognized. The phantom is a way of handling transient subassemblies that are usually not inventoried. As we incorporate JIT thinking into our production process, the question of residual inventory is reduced and the need for phantoms is minimized.

Other situations often occur that cause the need to identify a group of parts that cannot be assembled. This commonly happens when a bill of material is being modularized, that is, grouped by option sensitivity to allow forecasting and master scheduling on the option, instead of the end item level.

The Model Z Instrument

Let's look at an example we use in class, the Model Z instrument.

MODEL Z INSTRUMENTS

OPTIONS:
- Readouts   2
- Sensitivity Range   30
- Power Supply   4
- Transmitter Freq.   20
- Operating Current   5

Figure 2: The Model Z Instrument

The Model Z instrument mentioned earlier is a piece of electronic test equipment available with a number of options. There are four power supplies, 20 transmitter frequencies, two readout options, 30 sensitivity ranges and five operating currents.

How many possible end items are we dealing with?

Let's take a look:

2 X 30 X 4 X 20 X 5 = 24,000 possible end items

If the front panel can be customized for each customer, then the number of end items is infinite!

Under the traditional bill of material structuring, that means 24,000 separate bills of material, 24,000 end items to be forecast. Forecasting is never easy. If we happen to be selling 100,000 Model Z instruments a month, forecasting might be quite a challenge! Suppose our sales are only 20 Model Zs a month. Now forecasting which of the 24,000 motors we plan to sell is more than a problem, it's pretty close to impossible.

A solution to this problem is to forecast *options,* not *instruments.* If we forecast at that level instead of at the end item level (instruments), the number of items to forecast is significantly reduced.

Instead of 24,000 items, we have only 61 items:

$$2 + 30 + 4 + 20 + 5 = 61 \text{ items}$$

Sixty-one items to forecast and master schedule is a much more manageable number. The bill of material, however, must be reorganized to support this approach. The parts sensitive to a particular option must be grouped together, even if they can't be assembled together. This permits us to plan the right quantity of parts if that option is sold. A phantom part number identifies the group of parts. Again, the grouping may not be assembled— instead, it's more like a bag full of parts that apply when a certain option is selected.

We code this as a phantom, because the group of parts can't be built or inventoried. It gives us tremendous flexibility in planning and scheduling as well as maintaining the bill. Typically, there will be a phantom for the common parts, parts that are used in all assemblies. Should we need to change a common part, we'll only have to make that change in a single bill of material, that of the common parts phantom. Had we elected to use the original end item bill of material structure, we would have to make the changes in all *24,000* end item bills of material.

Customer Returns

Another common use of phantoms is for customer returns. This is a similar situation to transient subassemblies. When an item is returned and placed into inventory, we need a way to make that item visible to MRP II for planning and scheduling. That has been a critical problem for Centrilift, which regularly takes used oil well pumps back in trade. The pumps are broken down into either subassemblies or parts and placed back into inventory. Some returned items have parts numbers, others don't. The returns are coded as phantoms; as long as there is inventory on hand, material requirements planning doesn't blow-through to the gross requirements.

Phantoms And Pseudos

The term phantom was first introduced as part numbers and bills of material were put into computer records for MRP II. The exploded requirements had to be netted against the residual inventory of the phantoms. Also, the engineering bills included some subassemblies that manufacturing never made. In order to combine the engineering and manufacturing bills into a common computer record, those subassemblies were also added as phantoms. The term "pseudo" was introduced when forecasting and master scheduling options created the need to identify groups of parts common to the product or an option, although the parts group couldn't be built. Whether an item can or cannot be assembled, it is treated the same by the system. As far as the difference between the way a phantom and a pseudo are handled in the system, there really isn't any. There's no good reason to distinguish between the two. It just causes unnecessary confusion.

Phantoms give us tremendous flexibility...

All phantoms are added to the record just like any other assembly. Since the phantoms must be ignored at times, they require some special coding to facilitate the proper retrieval of the bill of material. When a phantom is added to the record below the master schedule level, the following steps should be taken:

1) Set the lead time equal to zero and make the order policy lot-for-lot; we don't want to actually build the phantoms.

2) Code the item as a phantom at the time it is added to the record.

3) Bypass phantoms during a material requirements planning run when the on-hand balance is zero. When the on-hand balance is greater than zero, the gross requirements should be netted against the inventory and the net requirements exploded to the components.

4) Pick lists or requisitions should not include phantoms unless the on-hand balance is greater than zero. The computer programs that retrieve bills of material and print the documents for

the storeroom should only attempt to use the quantities on hand in the stockroom. Most of the time, phantoms will not appear on the pick lists at all; only their components will be on the lists.

5) When printing single-level or indented bills of material, phantoms may be identified, as shown in Figure 3.

When the phantom is a master scheduled item, the same steps apply with the exception of numbers one and three.

Sometimes it takes a while for the phantom logic to sink in. Blue Bird, for example, initially balked at the phantom logic, but soon adopted it wholeheartedly.

"Our bills of material are set up using a modular concept— no true "0" level or end item ever exists," says Ray Dollar of Blue Bird. "A pictorial example of our bill would be a grocery store where items are logically grouped and displayed. The store would have items grouped by dairy products, meats, frozen items, bakery goods, paper products, etc. Within these major groupings would be smaller groupings or breakouts by size, type, etc. Our bills are *defined* by major items such as Engine, Axle, Tires & Wheels, Windshield, Bumpers, Entrance Door, Seats, etc., and are *structured* at the lower, more specific breakouts such as Engine Model and Horsepower, Tire Size, Windshield Configuration, etc. Our customer must select and order down to this level.

"Our modular structuring is necessitated by our varied product line and the fact that we build a custom product rather than a stock item," Dollar adds.

Blue Bird uses phantoms in its group bill of material system. The group bills handle items that vary by body length, emergency or exit door location, battery box location, body section arrangement and more, where the parts needed to build the unit vary by specific body plan configuration. Blue Bird has approximately 900 different body plans, each varying to some extent from the other.

"Items included in our group bills include side windows, floors, roof metal, book racks, floor coverings, etc.," Dollar says. "Each body plan can point to many group bills, but only do so if we have an order with the configuration which would call for a particular body plan/group bill."

COMPANY BILL OF MATERIAL

Level	Find No.	Part No.	Description	Qty. Per
..1	1	4500	Body	1
...2		5502	Body Casting	1
..1	3	J500	Welded Stem Assem.	1
...2		6501	Stem	1
....3		1234	Bar, 1" Rd; 316 SST	6
...2		9504	Valve	1
....3		1234	Bar, 1" Rd; 316 SST	2
..1	4	3300	Shims	4
..1 (Reference)		D290	Assembly Dwg.	1
..1	5	1010	Name Plate	1
..1	6	5050	Name Plate Screws	4
..1 (Phantom)	2	R007	Packing Set	1
...2		2000	Top Adapter	1
...2		3500	Bottom Adapter	1
...2		6200	Rings	4

Figure 3: An indented Bill of Material

Phantoms are just another tool for making the bill both work smoothly, filling each user's needs, and for accurately reflecting the way the product is made, helping to simplify the bill structure and planning and scheduling process.

Discussion Points

1. Discuss the definition of a "phantom item" and how it might potentially be used in your business.

2. Discuss the concept of looking at your product as several individual options rather than a single end item.

3. Identify examples where residual inventories frequently occur and how you might use phantoms to help manage these conditions.

4. Identify examples in your business, if any, where products are returned by the customer and subsequently disassembled, resulting in components that need to be identified.

5. Discuss the five steps for adding a phantom level and how they apply to your business.

Chapter 9

On Or Off?

What *do* we include on the bill? The real question is what can we afford to *exclude* from the bill, and if we exclude it, who's going to plan and schedule it?

The basic rule of thumb is to include everything on the bill of materials that needs to be planned and scheduled. This is, if the demands for an item are to be calculated and scheduled based on future requirements, the item should have a part number and be included in the bill of materials.

Here's a list of items that should be considered for inclusion on the bill:

1) Packaging material
2) Printed material
3) Instruction sheets
4) Manufacturing subassemblies
5) Hardware (bolts, washers, screws. etc.)
6) Semi-finished materials
7) Intermediates
8) Raw materials
9) Expendable tooling
10) Reference materials and drawings

Some of these are controversial items. The bill of material

has traditionally sprung from the engineering parts list. The engineering parts list is, in effect, a single level bill of material. It says what parts or items are needed to make a certain product. The engineering parts list might contain subassemblies that need to be broken down in a different way for planning and scheduling. Generally, the parts list will not include the specific raw materials or many of the other items on the above list.

The important fact is, though, that just because the printing or the tooling or the packaging is not being planned with the formal system doesn't mean it's not being planned. Someone is planning packaging or printing or tooling through an informal system. The safest way to guarantee you're going to have the parts you need, when you need them, in the right quantities, is to put all

---

The safest way to guarantee you're going to have the parts you need, when you need them, in the right quantities, is to put those parts on the bill of material...

---

those things on the bill of material.

Can a bottle of aspirin be shipped without the cotton ball that's stuffed in the top?

No, and that means that a shortage of cotton balls can tie up the entire assembly line. Does it make more sense to send old Joe down to Cotton Balls-R-Us every so often, or to put the cotton balls on the bill of material and have them there when you need them, in the right quantity?

We've already discussed the problem of the generator manufacturer who watched a huge shipment sit on the loading dock right through the end of the fiscal year because he'd run out of decals. We tend to forget that printed matter sometimes has a longer lead time than the product. Even an in-house printer can have press problems or backups. If you are planning and scheduling with the formal system, you won't find yourself trying to "expedite" your printer.

We tend to think of packaging in terms of smaller items, but what about shipping crates? Can you get the product off the dock if you don't have a shipping crate?

Centrilift requires special shipping boxes for its oil field pumps. Those shipping boxes have to stand up to everything from the rigors of overseas shipments to being hauled by helicopter to the well site.

"Without those boxes," says Dale Hendrix, "those pumps aren't going anywhere."

So the boxes are on the bill of material, plus any specialized cargo boxes or even the Styrofoam the pump is packed in.

Hardware, meaning small parts such as screws and bolts or even company nameplates and the like, should also be included on the bill.

Pause for a sharp intake of breath. You mean, we have heard time and again in our classes, that we should include little bitty screws and washers that we buy by the *billion* on the bill? That's just plain silly!

That's exactly what we're saying. Again, just because it's not on the bill doesn't mean that someone isn't planning and scheduling the item. It just doesn't happen to be your planners.

Small items such as screws or nameplates can be planned and scheduled just like the large, more costly items. For Manufacturing, however, such items can be bulk-issued from the stockroom. Instead of issuing two screws for each item, the stockroom can issue a box of 10,000 screws. When the 10,000 run out, the floor supervisor can get another box.

In a similar vein, there are some items that, on the engineering parts list, have their quantity per parent number listed as A/R, "as required." This is usually an item such as a washer or a spacer of some sort. What "as required" usually means is, "I can't figure out how many we need; see if you can."

Sometimes, the "as required" is a code word for a breakdown in communications between Engineering and the shop floor.

"We used to have a lot of 'as required' on our pump assemblies," says John Bearden, engineering manager at Centrilift. "We used the 'as required' for sleeves that went on the pump assemblies. Up in Engineering we always said it took two of the washers, but the guy who built it said it took three. Now we've replaced the `as required' with the shop floor's three."

In a case where the number of parts does vary, take an average and place that average on the bill. Then carry enough safety stock of the part to cover the high end, if necessary. That way you're getting the benefits of the formal system and still accommodating the way your product is built.

Semi-finished materials and raw materials belong on the bill of material for the same reason—planning and scheduling.

Expendable tooling is important on the bill because tooling wears out. When it wears out, the line shuts down and products don't go out the back door. We can schedule tool replacement just like we can any other component, which will minimize the down time on the line. The only other option is to stock an excessive inventory of expendable tooling, which, again, is money trapped in inventory.

Reference documents, instruction manuals, required operations manuals (such as with lawnmowers, firearms or other items facing potential product liability problems) and engineering drawings can also be listed as part of the bill. The advantage is that these materials will be available when and where they're needed. They must, of course, be given part numbers, but coded as reference materials so the system doesn't list them for picking and allocation. The reference documents can also be stored in the item master file and cross-referenced for an item. The advantage of putting documents and engineering drawings in the item master is that you need not worry about specially coding them as reference items on the Master Bill. The disadvantage is that, unlike the other materials on the bill, a special computer program may have to be written to exclude them from some printings such as the pick list.

As we mentioned when we started, the question in years past has been, "Why should we put these items on the bill of material?" The new question is, "Why shouldn't we put these items on the bill?" Every item that needs to be planned and scheduled should be on the bill, because if it's not on the bill, you risk not having the item when you need it.

Connaught Laboratories, for example, agonized over white mice. The mice were used for testing the product; without a requisite number of mice, the product couldn't be shipped. The decision was to put the white mice on the bill of material and plan

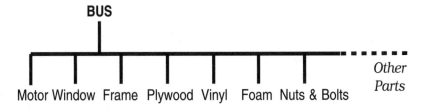

BUS

Motor Window Frame Plywood Vinyl Foam Nuts & Bolts   *Other Parts*

Figure 1: The Master Bill, including seat subassembly

and schedule them like any other item.

One potential troublemaker is service parts. When a part (or subassembly) is sold as a service part, it should have a part number and a bill of material. When an item is strictly a service part—not built, put in stock and later withdrawn for making the final assembly—it should *not* be included in the bill of material structure for the finished product. Instead, it should be treated as a separate item, with its own bill of material structure.

At Blue Bird, seat assemblies are normally immediately consumed during production, and, accordingly, are included in the bill as shown in Figure 1.

However, seat assemblies are also made for service parts. Blue Bird has created a second bill of material for the service part seat assemblies, as shown below. This helps simplify the Master Bill structure while accommodating the need for service parts.

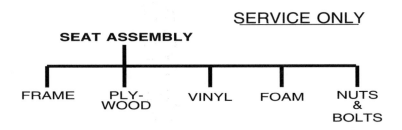

SERVICE ONLY

SEAT ASSEMBLY

FRAME   PLY-WOOD   VINYL   FOAM   NUTS & BOLTS

Figure 2: The seat subassembly B/M

Discussion Points

1. Identify items used in your product that are not currently included on your bills of material. Discuss why they are not included.

2. Identify both advantages and disadvantages of including the items identified in Point #1 on your bill of material. Estimate the magnitude of each advantage and disadvantage.

3. Discuss how items that are not currently included on your bills of material are ordered, planned and scheduled. Discuss the problems caused by not including these items on your bills of material.

4. Identify specific examples of service or spare parts that are frequently sold, but not stocked (see the School Bus Example) for use in the production of products. Discuss the advantages and disadvantages of excluding these items from the bill of material for the finished product.

5. Discuss alternative ways to structure the bill of material for the service parts identified in Point #4.

Chapter 10

The Advantages Of A Shallow Bill

There are three basic activities in bill of material restructuring:

- Adding or removing a level to the bill.
- Promoting and demoting items up or down in the bill's levels.
- Regrouping or rearranging the parts in the bill of material

When we're structuring a bill of material, we say that shallower is better. What that means is we want as few levels as possible in the bill.

There are clear benefits to having a shallower bill. Shallow bills are easier to maintain, meaning less work. And there's less paperwork with shallower bills. With a shallow bill, there'll be fewer work orders and fewer part numbers. There is, however, a more basic reason for striving toward a shallower bill:

An overstructured bill of material generally implies long lead times, unnecessary tasks, and, thus, higher costs.

Let's look at how that works. The simplest bill of material is

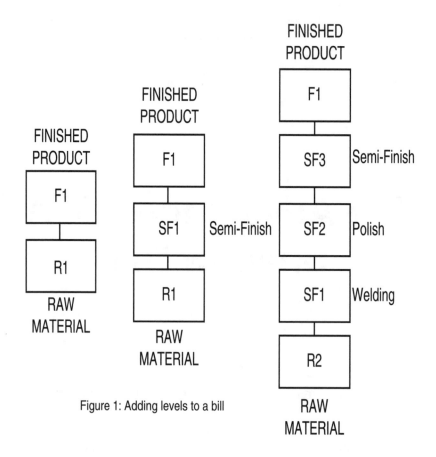

Figure 1: Adding levels to a bill

two levels: Raw material and finished product. You get the raw material in and perform four operations—weld, polish, final finish and package—to create the finished product.

At some point you decide for a variety of reasons to inventory the product in a semi-finished state, maybe you've made the welds but haven't had a chance to polish the weld. In order to inventory the semi-finished product, you assign it a part number. It's then checked into and out of inventory. You now have a three-level bill:

Cost Accounting has a couple of problems. They would like to know the amount of work accumulated at each of the three workstations—welding, polishing and final finish. A quick way to do this is to assign semi-finish part numbers to the other two work stations, then move those items in and out of inventory—if that isn't done physically, at least paper transactions are taking place. Labor reporting from the floor is used to accumulate cost for each semi-finished item part number. Accounting will then have a clear view of what's happening at stop in manufacturing. The bill has now grown to five levels.

In the beginning, our shallowest bill, the raw material flowed through the three workstations. There were only two inventory transactions—we issued the raw materials from inventory, and we checked the finished product into inventory.

> Ripples from added levels grow until sometimes they achieve tidal wave proportions...

When we added the third level to the bill, we also added a second work order and two additional inventory transactions. It also required an additional part number for a planner to review, reschedule, release the work order and maintain the planning data.

When we added two more levels to accommodate Accounting, we also added two additional work orders and four additional inventory transactions.

We added three additional part numbers for the semi-finished items.

The Consequences Of Levels

Levels in bills are like the ripples from a stone thrown in still water. They rapidly spread out through the entire company. Only, unlike the ripples, which are constantly decreasing in size as they move away from the event, the ripples from added levels grow until sometimes they achieve tidal wave proportions. The requests for accounting information in the above example translate into hours—and dollars—lost to paperwork and shuffling parts into and out of the warehouse. It also implies ha*ving* a warehouse in the first place, and the personnel to operate the warehouse. And a system to make sure you can keep track of what's going into and out of inventory.

There are numerous reasons we often rationalize (erroneously) for assigning a part number to a subassembly or semi-finished item and putting it in the bill. The three most frequent are:

1) We might want to be able to issue parts or materials from the stockroom in advance for that subassembly (often called staging) and find out if there are shortages.

2) We actually make the subassembly during the manufacturing process, although it is quickly consumed.

3) A drawing may be required, and it has a number. If the drawing number and the part number are the same, as we discussed in earlier chapters, you've created a part number by default! And the new "part number" requires a level in the bill.

Additional excuses for adding levels include "pay points," track WIP, QA inspection points, track scrap and yield in the process, collect labor costs and accommodate a change in lot size from one operation to the next.

Overstructured Or Understructured?

On the other hand, consider a machinist who makes a bolt from a bar of steel. Although there might be several intermediate stages, the machinist can see from the final drawing what he has to do.

The factory is an interlocking environment, and changes at any one point often have unforeseen and unplanned-for consequences at another.

> Remember, the process should dictate the bill of material, not the other way around...

Say there are four subassembly levels, each with a different part number, between steel rod and the finished bolt. Would such a bill be overstructured?

Well, the only answer we can give without studying the manufacturing process itself is, "Probably." You can't just look at a bill and tell whether it is overstructured or understructured.

That takes some analysis of not only the bill, but the manufacturing process. Remember, the process should dictate the bill of material structure, not the other way around.

In our bolt example, suppose the first subassembly level allows the machinist to finish the rod to a certain point, then inventory the intermediate, semi-finished bolt. In that case, the first subassembly level seems legitimate. Because the semi-finished item is going to be inventoried and needs to be planned and scheduled, it needs a part number and a level in the bill. Two other levels are, say, to collect costing information at those points. The information needed by Accounting can just as easily be collected on the routing, leaving the bill of material for its proper functions. However, we couldn't be certain until we looked at the shop floor. Possibly we need to consider changing the welding process to allow us to not have to inventory the semi-finished subassembly.

> The new system reflects the way products are made, not the way we think they're made...

The only legitimate reason for having a level in the bill between finished product and raw material is planning and scheduling!

Planned and scheduled does not necessarily mean stocked. We might want to plan and schedule only after we receive the customer order. This is called a made-to-order or non-stocked item. Made-to-stock, on the other hand, means items are produced to a forecast in anticipation of customer orders. We need part numbers for both stocked and non-stocked items.

I was walking through a plant one day and saw a bunch of parts piled on the floor. I asked the foreman what that pile was.

"Non-stocked parts," he said.

"What are they doing piled on the floor?" I asked.

"Waiting for more non-stocked parts to be put into a non-stocked subassembly."

I asked what the parts were behind the fence.

"Stock parts waiting to go into stock subassemblies," came the reply.

"What's the difference?" I asked.

He looked at me like I came from another planet. "*Those* are stocked," he explained, pointing in the appropriate direction. "And *these* are non-stocked."

The point is, both needed part numbers to identify the items.

A Questioning Process

Creating a shallower bill is part of the process of not only rethinking the bill of material, but rethinking how the product is built. The process for creating a shallow bill is a questioning process.

Examine every level in the bill.

Determine why that level exists.

• Is it for planning and scheduling?

• Is it an item that must be inventoried?

• Is it for accounting purposes?

• Is it to help collect labor costs?

• Is it there because it's always been there?

• Is it there to make it easier to stage parts to discover shortages?

• Is it because we have an engineering drawing?

• Is it there to help plan capacity and track WIP status?

APCOM's struggles to build a correct bill of material for its thermostat line is instructive.

As parts moved down the thermostat line, numerous subassemblies were created. APCOM's bill of material team, when it first began revamping the bill, looked at many of those subassemblies and asked the question, "What if we run out?" Although the subassemblies were created and quickly consumed, the fear of being caught without was a major factor.

There was also residual inventory—subassemblies that, because some matching parts were scrapped, the inventory was out of balance and the parts weren't consumed. Their inventory had to be considered when planning and scheduling production. Part numbers for these subassemblies were created and included in the bills.

"So we structured a bill of material that, I believe if you look at the initial one, was six levels deep. It was amazing," says a member of the team. "It was pretty impressive. We had pictures and drawings and stuff. It looked right."

The same logic was applied to the water heater element line; subassemblies were assigned part numbers for planning and scheduling. Charts were drawn. Everything looked good.

"Then we tried to start a work order system," the team member says. "We'd never had work orders before. Not a one. But with the new system, we had to have some method to fulfill all our requirements...So we sat down with the shop foremen and explained how it was all going to work.

"Fill out an inventory transaction for each subassembly when built and another when issued," the team member continues. "When you do this, an inventory transaction. When you do that, an inventory transaction. The shop foremen said, `Oh, really?'"

The shop floor refused to follow the new system, because the new system didn't really reflect the manufacturing process, which was more of a flow environment. The subassemblies were made but immediately consumed—not inventoried. And the inventory status of those fast-flowing items was not necessary to running the business.

"The new system reflected how we *thought* the products were made," the team member says. The shop floor *knew* how the product was made. "We were wrong...The bill structure we'd suggested would have increased our costs, slowed down product flowing through the plant and created a lot of pain and headaches. It's amazing what it would have done to this plant."

The result is a very shallow bill of material. This system accurately reflects the way APCOM's products are made, not the way everyone *thought* they were made.

"We make thermostats, not subassemblies."

Moving From Complex To Simple

In structuring a bill, we should train ourselves to move from the complex to the simple.

"Sometimes, bill of material and engineering problems are all tied up together," says Dave Biggs of Bently Nevada. "By cutting levels out of the bill to simplify the bill structure, we've also found it leads us to a simplification of the product. It gives us the right perspective."

Bently trains its engineers fresh out of school that they should strive for simplicity in design.

"Simplifying the bill is a big part of it," Biggs says. "It's not easy. It makes everybody have to adapt. People don't *want* to change."

Originally, most of Bently's bills were seven and eight levels. The average depth now is three levels. Many of the levels were actually operations. ("That's a trap a lot of people fall into.") All operations are now on the routing sheet. The main process of hammering down the levels in the bill took place at the manufacturing level. "We said, `Wait a minute,'" a Bently engineer tells us, "We told Manufacturing we didn't care how they built the thing. As long as they had the right parts in the right holes, they could have as many levels in the bill as they wanted."

Challenge every level of the bill!

The restructuring process is still going on at Bently Nevada, working back through existing product lines to examine every level in the bill—"I don't think we're ever going to be done," says Ray Bacon.

"When we first started out on the restructuring," says Bacon, "we had Data Processing go through the bill of material and pull everything with a level indicator of five or below. Then we printed it out and took a look at it with whichever production manager was involved. We went after the levels, examined them one by one, to see what we could remove...What we usually found was levels in the bill taking the place of routing numbers."

The simplification process pays other benefits as well. At Bently Nevada, the simplification process on the bill was so successful that it was applied to the routings. Routings with more than 12 steps were printed out and examined carefully to see if they could be pared down. They discovered a number of steps that could be consolidated or actually eliminated. The companies that have successfully revamped their bills have all gone through the simplification process.

Every level in the bill needs to be examined and challenged. If it is not there for planning and scheduling purposes, maybe it shouldn't be there at all. That challenge needs to be extended to the manufacturing process itself. Can we change the process so we don't have to move items in and out of stockrooms or inventory points, thus doing away with the need to plan and schedule them? If the answer is yes, then there goes another level in the bill.

The Impact of Simplification

The quest to be faster and less costly has caused manufacturing companies to focus on simplifying their processes. Some label

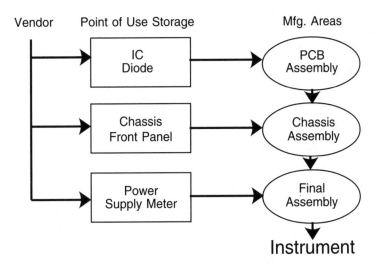

Figure 2: The Ideal Model Z Flow

the effort Just In Time; others call it continuous flow or re-engineering. In any case, one outcome of simplification is changes in the manufacturing process that eliminates the need for some

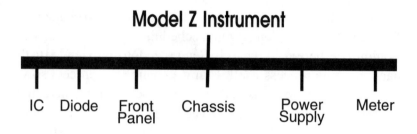

Figure 3: The Flattened Model Z B/M

levels in the bill. For example, in an earlier chapter we discussed a streamlined Model Z Instrument. (Figure 2, previous page). As we changed the manufacturing process, we moved to a shallower bill of material. In fact, our original three-level bill was reduced to a single-level bill. (Figure 3)

The volume of paperwork transactions was reduced by issuing materials in bulk from the parts stockroom to the point of use storage locations.

The inventory records were maintained with a technique called *backflushing*. That technique becomes increasingly useful—in fact, necessary—as we shrink lot sizes, a key objective of JIT.

The way backflushing works is simple: In the case of the Model Z, the number of instruments produced is reported. The computer "looks up" all items listed on the bill of material and reduces the appropriate inventory record for each item.

Simple!

One transaction from production to keep the inventory records up-to-date.

This approach, however, doesn't eliminate the need to keep accurate records—and an essential activity for accurate records is timely cycle counting and reconciliation of discrepancies.

Point-of-use inventories are, at best, tough to keep accurate. Frequent inventory record updates, then, are even more important to help with cycle count reconciliation.

In many cases with shallow bills, the need for timely inventory record updates imposes an additional hurdle when the bill is used for backflushing. For example, let's assume the printed circuit board (PCB) must go through a long "burn-in" and test cycle before it can be consumed into the chassis assembly and final assembly. It may be several days before the instrument is produced, thus several days before the POB parts are subtracted from their point-of-use inventory record.

Tilt!

The parts are gone, but the record shows they're still there.

Reconciling those records can be fun—and not likely done very well.

The solution is to add an additional data field to the bill of material record—op*eration used on.*

Production is reported at each stage. i.e., operation ten of instrument 2020; operation 20 of instrument 2020, etc. The inventory is relieved only for the components tied in the bill of material record for the corresponding operation number. The inventory record, then, is in sync with the material movement. This backflushing method is sometimes called *synchroflushing.*

Since the parts are used at different times, it may be desirable to plan the date of need for each component at different times. This is especially true when our JIT efforts pay off and our lead times shrink to days and minutes,

We now have more control and can fine-tune the planning, The need to know more precisely when materials are needed increases.

Conventional planning systems would "offset" the component requirements by the same uniform lead time. However, with our Model Z example, PCB chassis parts are needed a few days before the chassis, IC, diode, etc. This problem can be solved by putting a lead time offset factor in the bill of material record, as shown in Figure 4.

The date for component requirements is calculated by total

Parent	Component	Operation Used On	Lead Time Offset Factor
2020	PCB Parts	10 - PCB Assembly	0
2020	Chassis	20 - Chassis Assembly	6
2020	IC	30 - Final Assembly	8
2020	Diode	30 - Final Assembly	8
2020	Front Panel	30 - Final Assembly	8
2020	Power Supply	30 - Final Assembly	8
2020	Meter	30 - Final Assembly	8

Figure 4: Lead time offset

instrument time minus the lead time offset factor. In our example, the total lead time is ten days. The PCB parts are needed ten days before the instrument is due; the chassis four days before the IC and diode, etc. (Figure 4)

When products are produced on very long assembly lines and made from many different component parts, bills of material are often overstructured—additional unnecessary levels added. These levels are to accommodate timely backflushing, variable lead time offset requirements or physical issuing of components. Extra bill of material levels means extra bill of material maintenance, paperwork transactions and the whole host of other disadvantages already discussed. Shallow bills with the operation used on and lead time offset feature can give us the best of both worlds.

The accuracy of this data is essential to the effectiveness of this approach, which is another reason why all the bill of material users need to participate in defining their needs, understanding the tools available and be held accountable for an accurate bill.

"As we integrate JIT concepts into our MRP II system," says Dave Biggs, "the old control methods of keeping the bills accurate disappear. At the same time, the necessity for bill accuracy increases. We initially got the bills accurate by issuing kits made up of parts as listed on the bill. If the bill was wrong, the kit had the wrong parts and production stopped. The bills got accurate in a hurry! With JIT, we no longer issue kits. Instead, material is transferred in bulk to the shop floor, independent of the bill of material. The discipline to force feedback from the shop floor on bill inaccuracies has disappeared. Yet without proper planning, there wouldn't be any parts to issue! And proper planning depends on the bill."

JIT also impacted the way bill accuracy was measured.

"As we flattened our bills," Biggs continues, "we have more parts listed at level one. We have fewer bills and more opportunities on each bill for mistakes—and one mistake means an inaccurate bill."

For example, if a product has 100 subassemblies and each subassembly has ten components per bill, one subassembly bill can have an error, but the overall accuracy is 99 percent, If all the subassemblies are eliminated, and there is a single bill of material with 1,000 components, one wrong component means the bill accuracy drops to zero, using the conventional methods of measuring bill accuracy.

As we make the bills more shallow, the accuracy measurement must change, For example, the percent-age of wrong parent/component relationships may become a better method to track accuracy.

Discussion Points

1. Draw a bill of material structure "tree" for one of your typical products. Discuss why each level is currently created.

2. Find an example, if one exists, of a bill of material with more than three or four levels. Discuss if each level is truly needed. In other words, is it a legitimate level in the bill of material?

3. Discuss specific examples, if any, of current practices where bill of material levels are created but could be eliminated.

4. Discuss specific advantages if some levels in your bill of

material could be eliminated. Estimate the cost savings by eliminating these levels.

5. Discuss the impact of measuring bill of material accuracy when items are no longer issued by using pick lists created from the bill of material.

Chapter 11

Coping With Multiple End Items

Let's go to the grocery store.

You think *you've* got inventory problems! The grocery store manager's inventory is changing colors on a daily basis. No one wants to buy black bananas or hamburger that's a little green. There are customer service problems, too. When a bunch of guys from the factory drop in after work, they don't want to hear that their favorite six-pack is on "back-order." So the grocery store manager thinks to himself, "Hmmm, I've got inventory problems, and I've got customer service problems." In walk a consultant and a computer salesman.

"We've got just the thing for you," they say. "MRP II helps you cut inventory and improve customer service."

"Great," says the grocery store manager. "I'll take one."

"It's not that easy," the consultant says. "First, you've got to make up a master schedule for your end product. And, by the way, what is your end product?"

"Bags of groceries," the grocer says.

"How many do you have," the consultant asks.

"Lot's of 'em," says the grocer.

The consultant sees that the obvious solution is standardization, a standard bag of groceries. Maybe a standard bag for a family of four, a standard bag for a picnic lunch, a standard bag for a working mother with one kid.

The grocer likes the idea, and the three immediately set to work to produce a standard catalog of bags of groceries. Things are going great until someone comes in and asks for a picnic bag, only instead of chips, could he please have pretzels?

Pretty soon, the grocer stations a bagboy at the door, whose job is to check each bag and see if it's a "standard." If it isn't, the bagboy assigns it a part number and creates a new bill.

The computer salesman is happy. The consultant is happy. The grocery store is well on the way to bankruptcy.

What was the grocer's fundamental mistake?

He doesn't sell bags of groceries. He sells milk and butter and eggs and beer and meat and all the other products in the grocery store, which he then assembles into a bag of groceries for the customer's convenience.

Why Multiple End Items?

Let's say we put a suggestion box out in the lobby of our own business, and over the suggestion box we put a sign. "What," asks the sign, "should we do about the number of different end products we offer?"

The box will fill up overnight. We pull out the first suggestion, and it's from Manufacturing. Their idea is to eliminate all options altogether—make one standard product without any variations. Efficiency would be great, and quality would be top notch! Planning and Scheduling thinks that's a wonderful idea, and they've wholeheartedly endorsed this suggestion. It will be a snap to plan and schedule a single item. Purchasing, Engineering and Order Entry all suggest the same thing—get rid of options, build a standard or just a few standard products, and things around the factory will be a lot smoother.

Of course, there's one last suggestion in the box, and it's

from Sales and Marketing. It's a pretty simple suggestion. It says that if we don't add 10 new options in the next 30 days, the customers may eliminate all the headaches with one exception—keeping the sheriff's padlock off the front door!

Guess which suggestion we should act on?

Options have a way of making life difficult; the more options, the more difficult.

Standing on the loading dock of one factory I visited, I noticed that not a single item to be shipped was the same. I asked the shipping foreman if all the items were different.

"Yep," he said.

I asked if the company didn't have any standard products.

"Sure," the shipping foreman said. "They're the products in the catalog that nobody *ever* buys!"

> Options have a way of making life difficult--the more options, the greater the difficulty...

Customized products are a response to the marketplace. "We want it our way" is the market mandate. The "standard" is top be special. We add options—make it in orange with red stripes, give it an automatic transmission, offer it with strawberry flavor—because the market wants that product flexibility, and if we're not responsive to the market, we're no longer in business.

The challenge comes in how we handle multiple end items created by customer requests for specials. In essence, a special is a combination of options.

One plant I worked for early on had this problem. We knew we had a product with lots of options, and we knew those options could be combined to give us many end items. We decided that we'd be just a little smarter than the average person, and we'd solve our problem by applying the old "80-20" rule. The 80-20 rule dictates that 20 percent of the end item numbers will account for 80 percent of our business. In other words, all we needed to do was structure that 20 percent, and we'd be ready for 80 percent of our customer orders. We'd wing the other 20 percent.

We set up what started out to be a little group to structure end item bills of material. The group kept getting bigger and bigger. The job kept getting bigger and bigger. Our engineers soon discovered that they could take a copy of the bill, delete a couple of components, add a couple of other components and have a whole new end item bill. Pretty soon, we were carrying boxes of bills of material to the computer room to be keyed in.

When we purchased our computer system, the salesman told us we were buying "infinite capacity," unlimited storage capacity. The data processing manager came in one day and told us we were going to reach "infinite capacity" in October.

Apparently, Plan A wasn't working.

So we went back to figure out just how many end items we were talking about, and we discovered that in one product group alone, there were *five million* end items! Twenty percent of five million was still one million end items. As far as bills of material go, one million and five million are the same number—impossible.

Suppose we managed to load a million end-item bills of material into the computer, and it certainly is possible. Imagine trying to use one million bills of material, maintaining them, keeping them accurate, making sure the shop floor and cost accounting are using the correct bill. Even finding the correct bill to match the customer order wouldn't be a small feat. It simply won't happen.

Standardizing On Standard Items

Can we solve the problem of many end items by building a "standard" item?

Standardization is often touted as the ultimate solution to the option question, but as we can see from the above suggestion box, standardization seldom works. Who gets to pick what's standard—Manufacturing, who wants what's easiest to manufacture; Engineering, who wants what's easiest to design and maintain; Sales and Marketing, who wants the strongest item for the marketplace regardless of manufacturing and design problems;

Planning and Scheduling, who'd like plenty of customer lead time?

The answer is, "None Of The Above." The customer picks, and if the customer doesn't like your standard product, your competitor will have a field day with this opportunity.

When Henry Ford started out building automobiles, he offered any color the customer wanted—as long as that color was *black*. He didn't do that out of a love of the color black, but to simplify a fledgling manufacturing process. Detroit didn't begin adding options like they were going out of style for fun, but to attract a larger share of the market to their product. The fact that, many times, Detroit offered the *wrong* options only shows how critical the situation can become.

Options become a problem when the customer lead time is shorter than the manufacturing lead time. If customers are willing to wait long enough, there's no problem. If a customer wants to purchase a new automobile with gray paint, a V-6 engine and a stereo tape deck, and the customer is willing to wait the full length of time it takes to purchase the materials, fabricate and final assemble the car, no problem.

> As far as bills of material go, one million and five million are the same number–impossible...

We simply create a bill of material for the gray car with the V-6, the stereo tape deck and all the other parts necessary to build the car, then order the parts, plan the production run and build the car. If that happens to take six months, so be it!

But what if the customer isn't willing to wait? What if the customer insists on taking delivery in *one week*?

That means in order to meet that customer's needs, we have to forecast the options as well as all the other parts before we receive the order. But there may be thousands, or even, as in our case, millions of option combinations.

What's the best, most efficient way of structuring the bill of material in a situation like this?

There have been lots of strategies for handling products with many potential end items, including standardization. Maybe the components can be produced to a subassembly level, then assembled to order when a customer order comes in. As mentioned earlier, some companies apply the 80-20 rule. In some cases, companies actually build a standard end item, inventory that item, then pull it out of inventory and make the changes to it when customer orders come in. There are few things in manufacturing more harrowing than watching a crew haul something out of inventory and try to refit it to meet a tight customer deadline.

Others keep a few "standard" bills and try to add and delete to create the custom bill when they receive each customer order. These "standard" bills are usually previous customer orders—errors and long lead times are inevitable.

The drawback to all these systems is that they make Planning and Scheduling's job harder. They also mandate lots of inventory. By bringing components up to a subassembly level, you have to guarantee that not only will you have enough subassemblies in stock to fill the anticipated customer orders, but you also have to have enough of *all* the other parts in inventory to finish fabricate the items.

And what about quality—our key to competitiveness? Refitting is a waste of material, capacity and time—the ultimate non-value-adding activity—plus increasing the chance you'll have a warranty claim.

The Key To Coping

Modularizing is the key we're going to use to build a better bill of material for multiple end item products. The situation is the same for an automobile or for the bag of groceries—we're not building a gray V-6 with a stereo tape deck, we're building V-6s and stereo tape decks, which we happen to assemble as cars for the customer's convenience—at least, that's the way we need to plan and schedule. We need to plan and schedule on the option level, not the end item level.

When we group components by their option sensitivity, we

are said to be *modularizing* the bill of material.

A modularized bill gives us much more flexibility in planning and scheduling. We also drastically reduce the number of items we need to plan and schedule. Instead of forecasting the total number of end items, we are forecasting only the number of options. For example, if an item comes in two colors in four sizes in 10 materials, that's 80 end items (2 X 4 X 10) to forecast and schedule. If we drop down a level and forecast on the option level, there are only 16 items (2 + 4 + 10) to forecast and schedule.

> When we group components by option sensitivity, we are said to be modularizing the bill...

In fact, we don't necessarily even need an end item part number. Many companies with multiple end items don't even try to identify all the possible end items. Instead, they use a modularized bill of material and an efficient order entry system to create a unique bill of material for a specific customer order. That order number becomes, in fact, the end item part number. Once the order is shipped, a hard copy of the order number and its unique bill of material are stored in hard copy in case of the need for repair parts or configuration history.

Of course, eliminating end item part numbers isn't mandatory. You may still need to build to stock and place in inventory for immediate shipment. But the planning and scheduling for the materials is still at the option level.

Discussion Points

1. Identify an example in your product line where several options are offered. List the options. How many combinations of these options are possible?

2. Discuss the problems of forecasting demand for the products identified in Point #1.

3. Discuss how forecasting and planning the products and, thus, the component items could be done by option, rather than end product.

4. Identify other issues, such as order entry costing, etc., that need to be addressed if planning is done at the option level, rather than finished product level.

Chapter 12

Modularizing the Bill of Material

There's no such thing as a "modular" bill of material. A "modular" bill of material conjures up the idea of a bill with replaceable pieces, plug in and plug out modules. It's true we end up with something resembling modules, but that's not the whole story.

Modularize is a verb, not a noun. We *modularize* a bill of material, and the result is a bill of material that has been modularized. Referring to a bill of material as "modular" is a bit of verbal shorthand that is deceiving. In fact, you can't look at a bill and tell whether or not it has been modularized.

When we modularize a bill of material, we examine each part and determine its option sensitivity. The parts that are sensitive or dependent on the same option are grouped together. Instead of looking at the product from the end item perspective, we see it (as we mentioned in previous chapters) as a collection of items assembled or finished and manufactured for the customer's convenience.

It's the same sort of process American car manufacturers

have been going through for years. A sports sedan features the engine option, which includes a larger, more powerful engine, the handling option, which includes a beefed-up suspension and more powerful brakes, and a detailing option, which includes racing stripes, special paint and decals guaranteed to make the car go faster.

The reason to consider modularizing your bill is the same reason the auto makers package their options—sometimes it's unrealistic to stock every end item. Sometimes its impossible. Look at the companies we've already discussed. Blue Bird in Georgia has hundreds of options. When combined, they form potentially hundreds of thousands of unique buses. To build and stock in inventory 100,000 different buses is almost laughable; even if the company could afford it, where would they put them? How many millions of dollars in inventory would they be willing to tie up on the back lot? Which finished items should be inventoried, anyway?

Thousands Of Buses

An even more pressing issue is that suppose Blue Bird decided to build and stock 100,000 school buses, hundreds of acres of finished goods inventory. What do you think the likelihood is of some school district coming up with an all-new combination of options for a bus, a combination that Blue Bird doesn't have in inventory? In the real world of manufacturing, it's very likely. In fact, some production managers would say it's a dead certainty.

Despite a full field of buses, Blue Bird would be scrambling around, trying to "expedite" a special order bus. It might get a customer order for a bus with a specific engine, seats and transmission. The only problem is, the right engine is in a bus with the wrong seats. The right transmission is in a bus with the wrong engine and seats. The right combination doesn't exist, which means scrambling, or, in the worst case, disassembly of an already completed bus to get the right parts.

Modularizing the bill of material offers a way to deal with the problem of many end items.

The second critical factor in deciding to modularize a bill is customer delivery lead time versus how long it takes us to make the product. If a company builds to order, that is, does not begin to purchase materials or start assembly, finishing or fabrication until a customer order is in hand, the bill of material situation is fairly straightforward—with one important stipulation. That stipulation is that the customer is willing to wait the full lead time for the product. When we bring this up in our Bill of Material class, a lot of planning and scheduling people volunteer to go to work for this company.

> The likelihood of your being the only game in town in a worldwide market is getting smaller by the day...

Say it takes you 28 weeks to purchase materials, fabricate and assemble a piece of electronic equipment. Because you're the only manufacturer around who makes this particular piece of equipment, your customers are willing to wait the full 28 weeks for delivery. There's no problem here, even if you offer thousands of options. You get the order, go out and buy the parts, then start to work. Twenty-eight weeks later, the customer has the product and everyone is happy.

Notice, though, that this is a *low-competition* situation. The likelihood that you're the only game in town in a worldwide market is small and getting smaller by the day. In fact, if you're in this situation now, chances are you're already looking over your shoulder for the new guys, who are willing to offer deliver in 20 weeks, or even 10 weeks or 10 days.

A Point To Consider

Another point to consider before you modularize your bill is the total number of items manufactured each month (or whatever time period). If your product has a 100 variations, and you're manufacturing 10,000 a month, the planning situation isn't that tough. If, on the other hand, your product has a 100 variations, and you manufacture 10 a month, your bill is a candidate for modularization.

Let's look at another extreme. Centrilift in Oklahoma sells pumps to the oil industry. The pumps, which sit in the bottom of oil wells, are tough to manufacture, and total manufacturing lead time (including purchasing) can be as much as four or five months. The customers—major oil companies around the world—expect, actually, demand, delivery in a couple of days or less. If Centrilift can't deliver the right pump in the amount of time it takes to helicopter the pump to the well, there are other competitors around the world who will.

One of the traditional solutions to this dilemma in some companies has been to maintain a large inventory, but there are a couple of other wrinkles to this story. For a start, tying up large amounts of money in inventory is an invitation to business suicide. An even tougher situation for Centrilift is that there is no such thing as a "standard" oil well pump. There are hundreds, even thousands, of different varieties of pumps.

It's more than just a paper dilemma. Centrilift's ability to compete effectively in a world market is the difference between success and bankruptcy, and excess inventory adds costs.

Part of the company's solution was to modularize its bills of material.

"To meet the marketplace demand, we had to have the product ready by the customer's lead time, not our own lead time," says Dale Hendrix of Centrilift. "So we went back, scratched our heads and decided what we sold—a pumping unit, made up of pumps, motors and seals. Then we moved down to the next level to see what made up pumps, what made up motors, what made up seals. That was when we began to see the way to solve our problems."

The Overwhelming Advantages

The advantages of modularizing a bill are:
- *Better response time.* We're able to reduce the response time to customers because we're building the right products. We're

able to provide the right material to the shop floor at the right time.

- *Reduce costs.* A modularized bill of material is easier to maintain, reducing those costs. We're able to reduce our investment in inventory, because our better forecast accuracy allows us to carry less safety stock.
- *Reduce the number of master scheduled and forecast items.* For a start, the modularizing process aids in option forecasting. Instead of trying to predict every possible end item combination, your forecasters will only be predicting the option mix.
- *Faster and fewer errors in order entry.* The short cut of creating "special" bills by adding to and deleting from a standard bill are avoided.

For example, a company manufacturers police radios, and there are a number of options. There are three types of microphones, five mountings, five brackets, eight transmitting and eight receiving frequencies, three speakers, two squelch controls and four cases to choose from. (Figure 1)

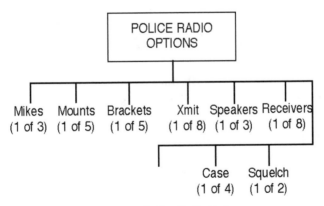

Figure 1: Police Radio Options

In fact, by multiplying all the options together, we discover there are 115,200 unique end item police radios:

$$3 \times 5 \times 5 \times 8 \times 8 \times 3 \times 4 \times 2 = 115,200 \text{ unique radios}$$

Traditionally, we'd have assigned each of those 115,200 radios a part number and a bill of material, a situation that makes computer salesmen's eyes light up with glee at the thought of all the data storage needed. And imagine the impact if Engineering adds one more option! It's now 330,400 radios.

Instead of looking at those 115,200 end items, though, let's move down to the second level, the option level. By adding all the options together—

$$3 + 5 + 5 + 5 + 8 + 8 + 3 + 4 + 2 = 38$$

—we discover that there are only 38 items on that level. Instead of planning and scheduling the 115,200 end items, we can plan and schedule the 38 items on the option level and still be able to assemble any of the 115,200 radios.

Which do you think would be easier: Forecasting 115,200 end items or forecasting 38 options? Instead of forecasting an end item, you're forecasting the total number of radios and the percentage of time an individual option will be used, which is much easier to do.

Overplanning Options

Modularizing your bill also allows you the option of overplanning certain options. Say there's a lot of variation on one particular option. Historically, 20 percent of your customers select this particular option, but there's been a lot of uncertainty in the market, and there's a chance that percentage will go up. A modularized bill allows you to focus the overplanning only on a specific option, accommodating item market demand fluctuations. At the same time, it wasn't necessary to overplan the other options that experienced less uncertainty in demand. The risk you take, of course, is ending up with some of the option items in inventory, but remember that planning and scheduling is a dynamic process, being monitored on a daily—and sometimes hourly—basis. Careful monitoring of the master schedule will help to keep inventory at a minimum.

There are also fewer bills of material with a modularized bill. Instead of 115,200 bills of materials for the police radios, we have 38. And if Engineering should add that one more option, it only adds one more bill, not 115,200. Some companies report a 90 percent reduction in the number of bills of material after modularization.

That, of course, leads to less bill of material maintenance. The harder it is to maintain the bills of material, the less likely we are to keep them up to date and accurate. Imagine having to go into hundreds or even thousands of bills and change part number X2224 to part number A1777. Even with computer global search and replace functions, it's much easier (and safer) to make a single change in the one bill of material for the specific option that includes part number A1777.

Another major benefit from modularizing the bill is more efficient order entry. Instead of a bottleneck that has Engineering and Production pulling out their hair, order entry can become a streamlined process. If necessary, the final bill of material for the end item can be created when the customer order is received.

Modularizing your bill allows you to forecast and plan at a level below the end item, which, in turn, allows you to plan and schedule fewer items. From a planner's standpoint, the fewer items to plan and schedule, the better.

Despite its uses, modularization isn't a miracle cure for every bill of material problem. We've had people in the Bill of Material class agonize over modularizing their bill, only for us to discover that they had only one product with a very limited number of options.

Remember the two criteria for modularizing the bill:
- *The manufacturing lead time is greater than the customer delivery lead time.*
- *Forecasting end items is not practical.*

Steps To Modularize The Bill Of Material

There are six basic steps to modularizing a bill of material:
1) Identify the family group.

2) Identify the options.

3) Look for the option sensitivity.

4) Create the Master Bill of Material.

5) Create the planning bill.

6) Create the end item bill.

Step 1: Identify the family group.

The first step in modularizing a bill of material is to *identify the product group*, or the family.

Let's take the example of the Sure-Fire Lawnmower. The product group is Sure-Fire Lawnmowers, and there are eight separate products—four 18-inch cut lawnmowers, four 21-inch cut lawnmowers.

PART	QTY.	B/M 101 x 1 18 in. cut 2 cycle Auto start	B/M 101 x 2 18 in. cut 2 cycle Manual start	B/M 101 x 3 18 in. cut 4 cycle Auto start	B/M 101 x 4 18 in. cut 4 cycle Manual start
Handle	1	H123	H123	H123	H123
Housing	1	B542	B542	B542	B542
Wheels	3	W890	W890	W890	W890
Blade	1	B765	B765	B765	B765
Muffler	1	M440	M440	M440	M440
On/Off Switch	1	S105	S105	S105	S105
Throttle	1	T880	T880	T880	T880
Engine	1	E220	E220	E420	E420
Shaft	1	A150	A150	A250	A250
Starter	1	X310	X410	X310	X410

PART	QTY.	B/M 101 x 1 18 in. cut 2 cycle Auto start	B/M 101 x 2 18 in. cut 2 cycle Manual start	B/M 101 x 3 18 in. cut 4 cycle Auto start	B/M 101 x 4 18 in. cut 4 cycle Manual start
Handle	1	H123	H123	H123	H123
Housing	1	B606	B606	B606	B606
Wheels	3	W890	W890	W890	W890
Blade	1	B987	B987	B987	B987
Muffler	1	M440	M440	M440	M440
On/Off Switch	1	S105	S105	S105	S105
Throttle	1	T880	T880	T880	T880
Engine	1	E220	E220	E420	E420
Shaft	1	A350	A150	A450	A450
Starter	1	X310	X410	X310	X410

Figure 2: The Sure-Fire Lawnmower Bills

With only eight end items, creating a bill for each end item is not a problem. But the modularization process is the same for much more complicated items, so let's step through it.

Step 2: Identify the Options

Step two is to *identify the options*. In the case of the Sure-Fire

Lawnmower, there are a number of options. As we mentioned, with the Sure-Fire there are two sizes, 18-inch cut and 21-inch cut. Each size is offered with a two-cycle or four-cycle engine and automatic or manual starter. (Sometimes this is called an *option within an option*.)

We find there are a total of six options—two sizes, two engines and two starters.

Step 3: Determine Option Sensitivity

Next, we begin to *determine the option sensitivity*; that is, we look at each component part and determine which option causes the part number for one component to be different from one lawnmower to the next.

For example, the housing is different for 18-inch cut and for 21-inch cut. Therefore, the housing is sensitive to the mower size. The blade is also sensitive to the mower size. The starters are sensitive to the auto or manual start option; the engine is sensitive to the two-cycle or four-cycle option. The complete list looks like this:

18-inch cut:
B542 Housing
B765 Blade

21-inch cut:
B606 Housing
B987 Blade

Two-cycle engine:
E220 Engine

Four-cycle engine:
E420 Engine

Auto start option:
X310 Starter

Manual start option:
X410 Starter

You'll notice there are a number of parts that do not change when the options change. These parts are *common* to all six versions of the Sure-Fire Lawnmower. We group these parts under a common heading:

Common Parts:
H123 Handle
W890 Wheels
M440 Muffler
S105 Off/on switch
T880 Throttle

In some cases we may find there aren't any common parts (perhaps the result of the engineers' creative minds working overtime). This doesn't mean that modularizing doesn't apply. Finding common parts is a bonus, not a necessity, for modularizing the bill of material.

You'll also notice that the shaft doesn't fit into any option category. Shafts A150, A250, A350 and A450 are sensitive to a combination of the size of the cut and the cycle of the engine. For example, larger cut mowers require a stronger, bigger diameter shaft, and four-cycle engines require a longer shaft. A shaft for a four-cycle, 21-inch cut lawnmower must be larger in diameter *and* longer than the shaft for an 18-inch two-cycle mower.

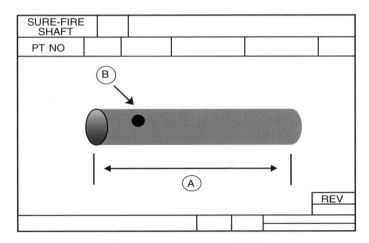

Figure 3: The Lawnmower Shaft

What should we do about this part? We have several alternatives:

1) The ideal solution is to go back and redesign the shaft and make one size fit all. The shaft would then become one of the common parts group. Inventory would be minimized, cost reduced, and there would be less chance for quality problems, since we only have to learn how to make one shaft, not four.

2) We can go back and review the manufacturing process itself. Maybe we could fabricate the shafts to a semifinished stage and keep them in inventory. After we get a customer order, the shaft could be finished to the right length and diameter as part of the final assembly process.

> By modularizing the bill, the forecasting problems have changed–mostly for the better...

3) We might not be able to do anything—it is possible that this shaft is very specialized and we have to live with the multiple versions. In this case we must forecast what percentage of the lawnmowers will use each individual shaft. The problem is that forecasting a combination of options is tough. We could protect ourselves by overplanning and carrying extras of all four shafts, which, again, may be the only alternative.

Modularizing the bill of material helps to isolate opportunities for standardizing and changing the manufacturing process for more efficient production. In modularizing the bill, we were able to see our product, the Sure-Fire Lawnmower, from a different perspective.

Step 4: Create the Master Bill

Now that we've got the parts grouped by option sensitivity, we assign each grouping of parts a single part number, creating a phantom level. Instead of five common parts to plan and schedule, for example, there's a single part number—say, C100—to plan and schedule (Figure 4, next page). Notice that we don't build a subassembly called C100, which is why we've coded it as a phantom. In fact, it's probably impossible to build such a subassembly. Instead, think of the phantom C100 as a bag of parts.

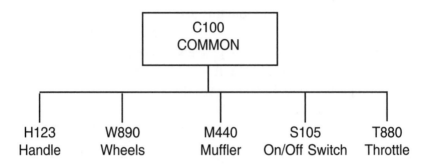

Figure 4: The Common Parts B/M

Another advantage is maintenance. Should we decide to make a change on the Sure-Fire Lawnmower's handle, replacing H123 with H124, we need make that change only on one bill of material instead of on eight separate bills.

We then create the *Master Bill of Material* for the Sure-Fire Lawnmower. The Master Bill of Material calls out all the phantom numbers and all the parts necessary to assemble the lawnmower. The master bill is the company database on the Sure-Fire Lawnmower. When we get a customer order, we create the complete list of parts for that unique lawnmower by blowing through the phantoms.

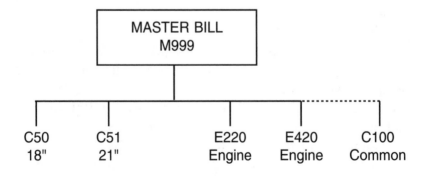

Figure 5: The Master B/M

Once we have the master bill of material, we can spin off the other bills necessary for the functioning of the business. The master bill is the one document that all the other types of bills—planning bill, final assembly bill—are all derived from.

Step 5: Creating Planning Bill

The first response when planning bills come up is one of consternation. There's only one bill of material, right, so what's this planning bill? Are we talking about creating another bill of material for use in planning, going back to the bad old days of multiple bills and confusion?

Not at all.

Planning bills do not require the creation of an entirely different bill of material structure. The planning bill is derived from the master bill. Its purpose is to help forecast demand for each option and, in turn, each part required for the particular option. What we've done in modularizing the bill is scramble the parts and rearrange them in a way that facilitates planning, translating the forecast or demand for options into individual components requirements. Because there's no such thing as a free lunch, we've got to do some juggling to come up with a way to use the new bill to, first, know what mix of products we're going to build, and second, know what and how many components to issue for the final assembly.

Planning bills are made up of the same phantoms, subassemblies or components used in the master bill, arranged in such a way to aid in forecasting. The planning bill, however, contains only the items to be forecasted and scheduled, while the Master Bill contains everything. For example, a product such as a radio might be designed to offer five mounting options, but we only forecast (for availability on a short lead time) two of them. The Master Bill, then, has the components for all five mounting options, while the planning bill has only the two to be forecasted and scheduled.

Let's go back to the Sure-Fire Lawnmower. There are, remember, eight versions of the lawnmower. If we plan to make 50 lawnmowers a month, how many handles, shafts, engines, etc., are needed?

That's a function of planning bills—to help translate the

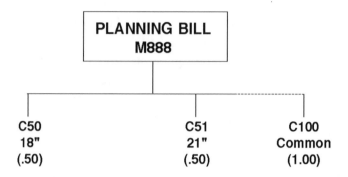

Figure 6: The Planning B/M

forecast of 50 lawnmowers into specific component demands.

In Figure 6 we see the planning bill documents that our forecast is for 50 percent of the 18-inch, 50 percent of the 21-inch and 100 percent of the common parts.

But by modularizing the bill, the forecasting problems have changed—mostly for the better. We need only forecast the total number of end items required, then forecast the percentages of the options. Forecasters don't have to predict the specific number of option combos. They don't have to say how many 18-inch, two-cycle, manual start Sure-Fire Lawnmowers are going to be built and sold, or which varieties of the 115,200 police radios are going to sell how many units. Instead, forecasting has to predict *total* number of end items—lawnmowers or police radios—then the percentage mix of options.

Historically, we might know that 75 percent of our customers prefer the four-cycle Sure-Fire Lawnmower. The other 25 percent purchase the two-cycle lawnmower. Eighty percent want the auto start; 20 percent want the manual start, and so on through the entire list of options.

To create the planning bill, we load those percentages, expressed in decimals, into the quantity per assembly field of the bill of material. The component forecast equals the total forecast (50) times the planning bill of material percentage (75 percent for four cycle). This is how the bill of material serves as a translator, translating the total forecast into the detail forecast requirements.

The common parts forecast is easy. It's 100 percent of the total. The option percentages are more difficult. Historical data helps. Any insight by Sales or Marketing further improves the prediction. Amazingly, we often find the actual percentages don't vary significantly over an extended period (three to six months).

Remember, planning bills don't describe an item that can be built. Rather, planning bills are a way of helping the master scheduler forecast demands. Also note that not necessarily all of the items on a planning bill are master scheduled items.

Companies tend to think of the planning bill as primarily a tool for companies that make to order. However, the planning bill is an equally useful tool for companies that make to stock. One example we use in class is the hockey glove. When the Canadian Cooper Company first came to the Bill of Material class, they were certain they made to stock, that they had no options. What they made was a hockey glove, and that hockey glove was made up of several parts—cuffs, gussets, backroll, thumb assembly, palms, laces, various striping material and so on. The gloves were also offered in a tremendous variety of colors—the customer could mix and match. The most popular color combinations depended on whoever won the annual Stanley Cup match!

Did the company have options?

Did it ever have options!

Cooper eventually decided to modularize its bill, assigning phantom numbers to the various color groups, then figuring percentages based on historical and market information. The company still makes the gloves and puts them in stock, but the planning bill concept was used to help make sure that the right components are in stock to make the right glove before the shelf is empty.

Other Uses Of The Planning Bill

Blue Bird used its planning bills to come to grips with the tremendous number of unique buses. From its Master Bill of Material, Blue Bird generated planning bills for the various component families. Based on comprehensive historical information, the company's marketing plans and an astute assessment of the market, Blue Bird's planners assigned percentages to the various options.

The company still had another hurdle to jump, though. Blue Bird has assembly plants not only in Fort Valley, Georgia, but also Iowa, Virginia, Canada and Saudi Arabia. Each assembly plant produces the same end items—buses—and each plant obtains components from the Georgia home plant. Although the bulk of the components comes from Georgia, each satellite assembly plant has its own special problems. For example, some of the plants have a certain number of components purchased locally. Each of the separate assembly plants has generated its own planning bills of material, which, in turn, drives the planning bill of material at the Georgia plant. Changes in the planning bill of material at any of the satellite plants changes the demand at the Georgia plant.

> The planning bill can be a powerful tool in managing your business...

Centrilift uses planning bills to predict the huge amount of returns that come back to its satellite "service centers," which are, in fact, mini-manufacturing centers.

It's the reverse of most planning bill applications, which predict demands, materials to be issued out, not in, to the stockroom.

The planning bill is a powerful tool to use in managing your business. Again, it's a derivative, sorted version of the Master Bill of Material, not a whole new structure.

Step 6: Creating the End Item Bill of Material

Let's take the Sure-Fire Lawnmower as an example for setting up an efficient order entry system. The most common system for order entry is the catalog. A conventional catalog lists all the part numbers and their specifications. For the Sure-Fire Lawnmower, then, SF-1 is an 18-inch, two-cycle, manual start lawnmower. To order a specific lawnmower, you just pick that part number or catalog number. When the order is entered at the Sure-Fire manufacturing plant, that specific bill of material is retrieved—either by hand or by computer. An alternative approach is to create an order entry menu that can be used to order by option instead of by lawnmower. The B/M is then created or configured for that specific customer order.

Let's arrange the order entry menu in an option-sensitive structure (Figure 8). What we're creating here is the same thing as a restaurant menu, with choices for entrees, side dishes and desserts. As you give your order in a restaurant, you're creating a unique bill of material for your supper. Using the order entry menu approach, you're creating a unique bill of material for a Sure-Fire Lawnmower:

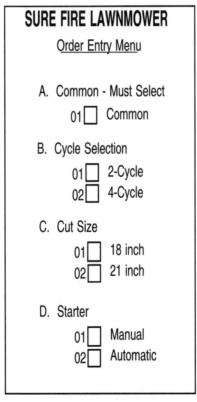

Figure 6: Sure-Fire Order Entry

The numbers after each selection are *configurator codes*. These codes *could* be arranged to create a unique part number and generate a bill of material for a specific Sure-Fire Lawnmower.

SF 01-01-02-02, for example, would define a two-cycle, 21-inch, automatic start lawnmower. This particular B/M is retained in an active file only while the order is active. After the product is shipped, the B/M is put in an archive for reference. This keeps the bill of material file from "growing." There are, however, disadvantages to using this as the part number, most notably the length.

Again, on a product such as the lawnmower, with only eight end items, assigning end item part numbers for order entry isn't a problem. But when there are hundreds of options with thousands of possible combinations, a menu driven order entry system is a lifesaver.

Order entry is sometimes a forgotten bottleneck at many companies (and, in fact, one of the reasons why order entry people need to be involved in the B/M restructuring team from the very beginning). The order entry system has usually grown from humble beginnings into a monstrous octopus, groping every which way. An order comes in from sales, and the order entry person begins frantically thumbing through spec books. Do we still make that? Can we make that? What's its part number? Have we had a sales order just like this before? Should we call Engineering? Don't we have a bill of material for that around here somewhere? Are those options compatible with that motor?

> Through modularization, we change the way we look at our product...

Order entry is a classic case of working smarter instead of harder. What we must do is link order entry to the modularized bill of material.

Before modularizing its bill, Centrilift was wallowing in a paper nightmare.

"We had all these paper copies," says Dale Hendrix of Centrilift. "Copies of the specs on pumps and equipment and things like that...Orders would come in, and we'd go through the paperwork. The order would go to Production, and we'd discover that a seal we'd obsoleted in a bushing was also used in the motor.

We'd revive it by going out and expediting it. The problem was we had to depend too much on the knowledge base of the people taking the orders. We had knowledgeable people out there, but the product changed so quickly..."

The situation was similar at Blue Bird. There was no catalog with every single bus with every single option listed. With more than 900 different body plans, there was no way to individually list every bus for a customer to choose from.

The solutions to both sets of problems are similar.

Through modularization, we change the way we look at the product as end items. In fact, there isn't necessarily a "0" level, an end item level, in the bill. Instead, we have bills for options.

At Blue Bird, for example, there are bills that group parts by options such as body length, exit door location, battery box location, side windows and the like. The groups, in turn, are gathered together under the specific body plans. Each of approximately 900 body plan Master Bills can point to many group bills of material for the various options, but only if there's a specific order for that particular body plan.

Configurators

A popular tool often used to link the modularized bills with the final assembly for a customer order is an automated configurator. In essence a configurator is computer software that translates the generic description of available options for a product into the appropriate part or bill of material numbers. The tool can particularly be helpful when many customer orders are received each day for products with many options, and end item or catalog numbers are not used.

Here is how configurators work. The option sensitivity for each part or bill of material number is linked in a computer record. When the options are identified, the software searches for all parts with that code. All parts or bills with associated codes for the individual customer are compiled, structured–or "configured"–into a single end item bill, unique for the customer order. Sometimes these systems are referred to as "Rules Based Configurators".

This means the selection of parts is based on rules to find parts or bills that are dependent on product options. Sometimes the parts are dependent on combinations of options. The creation of the end item bill becomes increasingly complex, and configurators are particularly useful. Some of the more complex configurators may even perform calculations and assign unique part numbers for special items. For example, one manufacturer of windows and doors use a configurator to determine the unique parts needed once a customer provides the door or window dimensions.

Configurators are not a short cut for modularizing bills of material nor do they eliminate the need to modularized the bills. The option sensitivity for each item still needs to be determined and documented.

A word of caution about configurators, though. They can be an effective tool to use *after* the customer order is received. A key to good customer service is to have material available *before* the customer order is received, so that delivery is quick. Therefore, the ability to plan, using planning bill concepts, is essential. Be sure this issue is considered before attempting to use a configurator.

The Blue Bird System

Blue Bird uses a configurator system. Their Order Conversion System analyzes each customer order and retrieves the bill of material or group bills of material for that particular order.

Remember the grocery store analogy in the previous chapter? Let's take it a step further. In Blue Bird's case, the customer enters the grocery store with a shopping list. The customer goes up and down the aisles selecting items (the Order Conversion System) in sufficient quantity and type (group bills) to match the shopping list. Arriving at the checkout stand, the customer will have some loose items, some prepackaged multiple items and some packages with items the customer selected by quantity. The Order Conversion System converts all those items into a final assembly bill of material for that unique bag of groceries, in this case, a completed bus.

A separate Master Table exists for each product line and

body type Blue Bird offers. Each Master Table has direct linkage to many sublevel Decision Tables, which actually analyze the order. The option that the customer specified (folding doors, for example) is matched against the multitude of choices, and the correct, unique bill of material is selected. The Master Table provides a directory of Decision Tables the customer (or a Blue Bird representative) must answer. The Decision Tables also handle the thorny question of compatibility, preventing the system from accepting an order for a combination of options that cannot be built.

It's basically a tree structure, common in order entry. But the advantage is that what we're actually creating is the bill of material for that particular product. That unique bill of material exists for that particular order only. Once the bus is built and shipped, the bill may be stored in the archives for reference. But it's removed from the active file. Using the computer, we can instantly recall the B/M given the customer order number.

For a company like Centrilift, this kind of traceability is critical. Each oil well pump may be slightly different, and when a pump is returned to the company—sometimes 10 to 15 years later—service technicians need the bill of material to know how to rebuild the pump. In addition, the order entry-modularized bill of material system allows Centrilift to track customers' special requirements very accurately, another facet of competing effectively.

In one of the offices at Bently Nevada there's a sort of shrine to a revised, modularized bill of material. The shrine consists of piles of old specifications books, enough paper to make any order entry clerk's life a living nightmare.

They keep the books around to remind them of the bad old days before a newly modularized bill and a special computerized configuration system made order entry easy.

Bently Nevada uses a sophisticated configurator system, its Customer Order Service (COS) system. According to the introduction in Bently Nevada's COS manual, the system was developed for four reasons:

• Catalog numbers, planning bills, part numbers and related

information were processed in a complex manner that required a great deal of manual activity. This resulted in excessive lead times, customer order errors, product structure inaccuracies and difficulties in processing customer and engineering changes.

- Separate uncoordinated procedures made it difficult to store, access and maintain all the information required to process and service a customer order. This had many adverse effects with respect to time, accuracy, cost-of-administration and customer relations.
- The original order entry system could not enter quotes for order clarification, planning, forecasting or prioritizing purposes. In addition, the rules for prioritizing customer orders were not clearly defined, understood, implemented, uniformly applied or correct.
- Timely and useful information about the business activities was not easily accessible or communicated. This included customer information, order status, change notification, education, documentation and bookings and commissions.

In other words, the old order entry system was a major hindrance in achieving the business goals. The new system edits the part number and the catalog numbers for valid part/catalog numbers, options and modifications. The edited entries, if valid, are then exploded to determine the parent-component structures. Once the structures are determined, the order is priced and filed for master scheduling.

Again, a tree structure is used. Bently Nevada uses what it terms long catalog numbers, which include a prefix number followed by a series of option boxes that hold the configurator codes. Such a number is used to describe "build to order" items (Bently Nevada also builds to stock). Each configurator code leads down to the bill of material for that particular option. By the time the order form is completely filled out, a complete bill of material has been created.

The COS system also handles compatibility questions, so, according to Bently Nevada, "We don't get bad orders out on the floor unless there's something wrong with our translator."

Another Advantage of Modularization

Here is a scenario often too frequent for make to order custom products. Sales person calls on the customer, commits to a price, commits to a delivery date and gets an order. Unfortunately, all of the information needed to make the product wasn't obtained. The omissions weren't intentional but are disastrous. Some of the omissions are discovered in the early stages of order entry. Now we have to go back to the customer and get the rest of the information. Some of the omissions are discovered while trying to do the engineering work. Some are discovered while trying to make the product or worse after the product is made or even shipped. Correcting the omissions are now are very expensive! The delivery time is extended. In some cases a large staff is needed just to correct the constant flow on incomplete information. The root cause of the problem is the sales person often doesn't know all of the questions to ask in order to get a complete definition of the product being sold.

Once the bills are modularized and the menu or configurator rules are established, the questions that need to be answered are clear. The odds that the customer order is entered correctly the first time are increased. The result is a tremendous savings in time and money.

Discussion Points

1. Discuss the meaning of modularizing a bill of material.

2. Discuss the two critical considerations for determining when modularizing a bill of material is likely to be advantageous.

3. Identify the customer delivery lead time and the total manufacturing lead time (including purchased lead time) for one of your product families where several options are offered.

4. Discuss the advantages of forecasting and planning at the option level, rather than the end item level, for these products.

5. Discuss each of the six steps to modularizing bills of material.

6. Discuss potential advantages of modularizing bills of material for products that have many options.

7. Identify an item (component part or intermediate) in your business that is manufactured or purchased in multiple configurations because it changes when different product options are specified by the customer.

8. Discuss the differences in master, planning and end item bills of material. Discuss how each of these bills are used and their interdependence.

9. Discuss what option sensitivity means and identify examples in your products.

10. When bills of material are modularized, sometimes a group of parts (called common parts) are identified. Is it essential that a product have common parts for the process of modularizing the bills of material to be advantageous? Please discuss.

11. Discuss how percentages in the planning bill may be determined for your products.

12. Discuss the advantages of using a menu vs. end item part number (or catalog number) approach for order entry.

Chapter 13

Building The Requirements File

Some of the problems that put stress on the formal system include:

- One-time B/M substitutions.
- Customer special orders.
- Engineering changes.
- Lot traceability or configuration control.

Fortunately, there is a tool to help us handle such bill of material problems within the formal system. The Requirements File is series of computer records that identify the unsatisfied demands for released or issued orders, or, if orders are not being used, an uncompleted quantity on the manufacturing schedule. In addition, the Requirements File can be used to tie a bill of material to a specific customer order.

This allows the Requirements File to be used to:

- Support one-time B/M substitutions.
- Help in configuration control.
- Help make one-time alterations to the quantity per for a single production run.

- Help determine the actual cost of an item.
- Allow overriding of normal lead times.
- Simulate a production run to test material availability.
- Support smooth engineering changes.
- Store a unique bill of material (sometimes called a one-time bill) for a given customer order.

One-Time Substitutions

One of the most common problems is also one of the thorniest, and that's the question of material substitution. Suppose it's getting near the end of the month and the factory floor is humming away. Just when you get ready to produce the last 100 widgets for the month, though, you discover that a batch of bad widget subassemblies somehow got through. You only have 75 widget subassemblies and you need 100. However, there's another subassembly from SuperWidgets that will work just as well, and you happen to have 25 in inventory, just enough.

It doesn't take a genius in production planning to figure out that you're going to substitute the SuperWidget subassemblies for the original subassembly to complete the last order.

The question is: How are you going to use your formal system to do this?

Of course, you could do it informally, send a guy out to the stockroom to get the SuperWidget subassemblies and deliver them to the factory floor. But let's look at what could happen.

For a start, when you start to build SuperWidgets, there's a discrepancy in inventory—25 SuperWidget subassemblies are no longer there. By using an informal expediting system, your formal MRP II system has no way of planning and scheduling the additional SuperWidget subassemblies to make up for the shortfall. You've laid the groundwork for another awful end of the month.

To one extent or the other, every manufacturer has to deal with material substitutions. Some industries, such as food processing, where the companies have to assay their raw materials as they're received, then mix and blend to bring the product up to the same level of product specification each time, substitutions or alterations to the quantity per are a way of life. In others, it may be a one-time occurrence. Still, the system must be capable of dealing with the problem.

The consequences of dealing outside the formal system are expensive and far-reaching. The reason we've gone outside the formal system is because we don't have a tool we can use to make one-time changes. The other factor is that such a tool must be simple to use. Despite our best intentions, we're not likely to use a tool that takes the better part of a working day to implement. It's too easy to send old Joe to the stockroom to get those SuperWidget subassemblies.

The Requirements File allows us to handle this one-time substitution within the formal system. The Requirements File is created by a series of computer programs that accesses both the Item Master and bill of material files. The result is that a record (stored in the Requirements File) is created by taking a "snapshot" of the bill of material and tying it to a specific order.

Sometimes the Requirements File is called a demand file or a file that contains the gross requirements from planned orders and firm planned orders.

We use the term Requirements File to mean whatever file is used to store the gross requirements from firm planned orders or scheduled receipts. Sometimes the Requirements File may be called the reservations file, the allocation file or the time-phased allocation file. The terms are synonymous. Sometimes a Requirements File is a part of the Item Master, or is tagged as an Order/Demand File. The planner involved with the Requirements File needs to input the following information to the system:

- Item number to be produced
- Manufacturing order number (or schedule, if manufacturing orders aren't used)
- Quantity to be produced
- Due date of the order

The computer will then calculate the following information:

—Quantity required for each component, determined by extending the order quantity times the quantity per in the bill of material.

—Start date for the order, calculated by backing up from the due date by the planned lead time for the item to be manufactured.

One important point is that changes to the bill of material must not automatically change the Requirements File. If they do, the effectiveness of the Requirements File approach is greatly reduced. Unfortunately, some software does automatically change the Requirements File after a change to the bill.

In order to effectively use the Requirements File, your system must be able to independently maintain (add, delete, change) the bill of material tied to firm planned orders or released orders (or schedule) independent of the Master Bill of Material. The system must also be able to use those changes in material requirements planning. It doesn't do much good to make the changes in the Requirements File, only to have MRP II disregard the changes and go back to the bill of material when recalculating gross receipts.

Let's go back to our widgets. A bill of material for our widgets looks like this:

Bill of Material File

Part Number	Quantity
A100 Widget subassembly	1
B100 Bracket	1
S200 Screws	2

The Requirements File takes a "snapshot" of this bill of material, multiplies the number of items needed by the quantity per and attaches the new file to the specific order number.

The Requirements File for an order of 100 widgets looks this:

Requirements File

Part Number	Quantity Required	Quantity Issued
A100 Widget subassembly	100	0
B100 Bracket	100	0
S200 Screws	200	0

The algebraic difference between the required quantity and the issued quantity is the gross requirement for the component. Because the Requirements File ties a bill of material to a specific order number, it gives us a way of altering the bill of material for that particular order without altering the master bill.

Suppose, as we said earlier, that we don't have enough A100 subassemblies to complete the order. We know, however, that a substitute part, the SuperWidget X100 subassembly, will work just as well. We also know that if we substitute the SuperWidget subassembly, we have to change the bracket to Y100 and the mounting screws to S350. The bill of material remains the same:

Bill of Material File

Part Number	Quantity
A100 Widget subassembly	1
B100 Bracket	1
S200 Screws	1

To make the substitutions, we go directly to the Requirements File and directly enter the changes:

Requirements File

Part Number	Quantity Required	Quantity Issued
X100 SuperWidget subassembly	100	0
Y100 Bracket	100	0
S350 Screws	100	0

Using the Requirements File, MRP II will make the adjustments, adding the gross requirements for the new components and deleting the gross requirements for components that will not be used.

It's important that a pick list be generated from the Requirements File, not the bill of material, for this manufacturing order. Otherwise, the shop floor will try to use the standard, not the substituted, parts.

The master bill of material has not been changed, and the substitution has been handled easily and effectively.

Configuration Control

In addition, widgets are routinely sold as service parts. In order to get the SuperWidget subassemblies to work properly, you also must replace Bracket B100 and Screws S200, as seen in the above example.

Unfortunately, you've replaced your entire service department since the widgets with the SuperWidget subassemblies were shipped, and, in fact, you've changed the SuperWidget subassemblies. When those widgets come back in for service, the new service technicians are at a loss. The widgets are assembled with the wrong parts! The repair department can't figure out what's happened. Nothing is what it's supposed to be. In disgust, the repair technicians rip out the SuperWidget subassemblies and replace them with the original assemblies.

Did we mention that widget subassemblies are only slightly less expensive than Cadillac sedans?

When customers need repair parts, we send out Bracket B100 and Screws S200.

They don't fit, and the customers are not happy.

That's a question of configuration control—what parts did we really use to build an item? Configuration control can be absolutely central to the production of the item (such as pharmaceuticals or foodstuffs). Or, as in the case of the wrong widgets, configuration control can be an important aspect of customer service. We need to be able to trace back and find out what parts were really used; this is called lot traceability.

The Requirements File helps support lot traceability. In some industries, such as the drug and food processing industry, lot traceability is a life-or-death matter. Companies must be able to track down every single pill of a drug that has been contaminated. The contamination might have occurred at any point, and it is important to know which raw materials went into which lot.

On a less critical but no less important scale, the lot-to-lot traceability aspect of the Requirements File allows you to give better customer service.

Let's go back to the widget example. When a widget comes

in for repair, the repair technician can pull an accurate bill of material for that specific order number, which would clearly reflect the substitution of the SuperWidget X100 subassembly. Should those widgets need repair parts, the correct parts could be sent out. The result is better customer service.

The Requirements File is only part of maintaining accurate configuration control, however. The shop floor must update the Requirements File, keeping an accurate, up-to-date record of what is really being used to build the product.

Changes In The Quantity Per

The Requirements File can also be used to alter the quantity per for a single run. This is most commonly done in food processing and chemical industries, where a greater amount of a component might be needed to offset a decline in quality (increasing the amount of sugar, for example, because of a decrease in the dextrose level of milk).

We might have a case, though, where the shop floor discovers that the quantity per is incorrect. Take the widget example. The shop floor might discover that a lot of brackets B100 have come in from a vendor that are usable but require four instead of two S200 screws. The Requirements File can be changed to reflect the need for those additional screws.

In fact, the Requirements File can handle any one-time deviation from the Master Bill of Material.

The Requirements File can also be used to store other important and useful information.

Generating The Pick List

The pick list should be generated from the Requirements File to guarantee that the substitutions in the bill of material are properly identified. When the material is issued, the pick list should be marked with the quantity issued and the list returned so the inventory files and the Requirements File can be updated as well, maintaining configuration control.

If pick lists aren't used to issue materials—a situation common in JIT environments when backflushing is used to relieve inventory—substitutions still must be accurately reflected.

The Requirements File should also contain the date required and the date issued for each component (calculated by offsetting from the due date the planned lead time). The planner should have the ability to override these dates.

The date required field provides another powerful tool for the planner.

The date required field gives the planner the option to allow a different lead time offset for some components in an assembly. In an assembly process, all components don't necessarily need to be there at the same time. In fact, obtaining all the components at the same time can result in the negative problem of unneeded inventory.

The solution is the date required field in the Requirements File. For example:

Required Components	Quantity Required	Quantity Issued	Date Required
B305	50	0	6/1
D145	50	0	6/1
R503	50	0	6/8

Notice that component R503 isn't needed until 6/8, and can be planned and scheduled accordingly.

As the bill of material is made increasingly shallow and lead times become shorter (as in a JIT environment), the need to show a different required date for each item on the bill becomes more critical. The lead time offset feature, as explained in Chapter 10, makes it possible to fine-tune the required date.

The issue date field is another handy check-and-balance item. Since the edit routines for updating the Requirements File often identify errors in reporting, it's helpful to have good traceability as to when partial issues of components occur. The date issued field allows planners to have a quick reference as to when the last issue was made.

Other Uses Of The Requirements File

The Requirements File is useful for accurate costing of production runs, since the Requirements File reflects what was actually used to build the product. If costing is done from the bill of material file, and substitutions have been made for this particular run, the costing will be inaccurate. In our widget example, suppose SuperWidget subassemblies were substantially more expensive than widget assemblies.

We can also use the Requirements File to run a simulation of a production run to check for any materials shortages. All requirements that have not been issued for a component are netted against the on-hand inventory. A "potential" shortage report is generated, showing which items would not be available.

The Requirements File is also a vehicle to handle special customer orders. The special material required by the customer is treated as a one-time substitution. The "special" bill of material is created and stored in the Requirements File or a separate customer order Requirements File. For example, a customer may request stainless steel screws for a unit operating in a corrosive atmosphere. We can handle the substitution through the Requirements File and use it for both configuration control and correct costing.

The Requirements File has other uses in managing engineering changes, which we'll be dealing with in a future chapter.

Discussion Points

1. Discuss the four typical problems listed at the beginning of the chapter (one-time substitutions, etc.) and identify which of each applies to your company.

2. Discuss specific examples of how the Requirements File approach may be used to solve some of your company's business problems.

3) Discuss how the Requirements File (or Records) might be created and used at your company.

4) Discuss the content of the Requirement File that could be helpful in your company

Chapter 14

Changing The Bill of Material

The bill of material never changes, right? It's carved in stone, handed down from the mount. Once a bill of material is totally accurate, it never changes.

Of course, that's a total fantasy. The bill of material is a dynamic document, reflecting the dynamic nature of products. Products change and evolve, getting better, which means we're better serving our customers' needs. We correct the rough edges, streamline our production, do a better job.

If that's so, why aren't people enthused about bill of material changes? If the changes are good, part of an evolving process geared to better customer service, why does the mere mention of engineering changes to the bill bring either a series of groans or a series of yawns?

Changes to the bill of material are a controversial topic. In our Bill of Material class, we've had some innovative suggestions on handling bill of material changes.

One manufacturing manager, for example, suggested that we just ban them outright—the old carved in stone theory at work. A second suggestion was that we rename "Engineering Changes" and start calling them "Engineering Mistakes." That should cut down the number of "Mistake" forms filed! A third suggestion came from one guy who'd noticed a correlation between the number of engineers and the number of engineering changes. The more engineers, the more changes. The solution? Get rid of the engineers.

Speaking as a former engineer, I'm not thrilled about the implications of that suggestion.

The problem with engineering changes is really several problems disguised as one. For a start, the basic problem is the volume of changes. One or two changes a year wouldn't amount to any problem at all. Dozens, or even hundreds, of engineering changes a month adds up to a nightmare. The second problem goes back to the second suggested solution, the "Engineering Mistakes" solution. Rather than thinking of changes in the bill as a good process, part of the process of getting better, there's a tendency to see the process as one of admitting mistakes, which no one likes to do. Better to keep the whole change process swept under the rug. Finally, bill of material changes, when handled incorrectly, tend to generate a lot of problems, which are usually blamed on something else.

> Changes to the bill of material are controversial topics...

Engineering changes are, as a rule, tough to control and hard to communicate to everyone who needs to know. When there are specific bill of material change policies, too often they're policies that looked good on paper, but are overly complex and may require the participation of people normally not available. If your bill of material change forms require a signature by your CEO, what's the likelihood that procedure is going to be followed to the letter?

Most companies don't have the tools for planning and scheduling in place, so it doesn't matter how the bill of material changes are made. The informal system didn't use the bills in the company database anyway—Sam down in the stockroom was the only person who knew how all this stuff worked. And even with the formal system in place, there's a question of overexpectations. People would just like to walk past the computer room, whisper in its ear that a change is coming, then walk away while the computer causes the old material to vanish and the new material to magically appear.

Problems From Poorly Managed Bill Changes

Perhaps the most significant cause of apathy toward engineering changes is a lack of understanding about the impact of those changes. It's not always obvious that the visible problems on the shop floor are a direct result of mismanaging engineering changes. Here are just a few of the problems that can result from poorly managed changes:

• *Excess obsolete inventory*: This happens all the time. There's inventory left over after the part has been obsoleted. Obsolescence is, unfortunately, a necessary evil; there's no system that's going to get rid of it entirely. However, well-managed changes to the bill can keep it to a minimum. If changes are poorly managed, it's not unusual to see obsolete parts reordered.

• *Assembly, packaging or finishing shortages*: You can't build it if you don't have the parts. Shortages often occur because we ran out of one component before the new component was ready or had been delivered. When the bill of material is not current, the wrong material is scheduled. A scheduling system is only as good as the bill of material!

• *Inefficient Production*: When engineering changes are not properly managed, the problem often doesn't surface until the 11th hour. Final Assembly discovers it is using Revision D. The latest engineering design is Revision E. The parts must be reworked or produced to the latest revision with zero lead time—bring in the expediters. Economical and efficient production is pushed aside until the crisis is past.

• *Missed delivery dates to customers*: Only items on the bill of material can be scheduled. When the bill is not updated with the latest engineering changes, the wrong materials are scheduled and produced. The problem is usually discovered in the final stages of production—and that's too late! Result—another customer delivery date rescheduled.

• *Poor product quality*: When the bill is not properly maintained, the latest product improvements from Product Engineering are not communicated to the factory floor. The hours of engineering effort to create a top-quality product are wasted.

• *Lack of configuration control*: Product liability has become one of the hottest issues facing industry. A quick short cut to a guilty verdict is failure to prove good control over the configuration of your product. Configuration control is ensuring that the bill of material and the material used to produce the product are one in the same. Configuration control is an unfulfilled dream when changes to the bill are not properly implemented.

> Documenting each change is the first step in bringing the system under control...

• *Lack of confidence in new product scheduling*: Nobody trusts anybody on new product scheduling. The product engineers might slip around the formal system and order the new material on their own. The shop floor might arrange to have extras of the old part, "just in case." Marketing is promising delivery of the new design without the slightest idea of when it'll really be available. Without a successful system making sure all the right items are available at the right times, phasing in and phasing out material or products becomes a disaster.

• *Erroneous product costing*: When the bill of material is not maintained, the product costs do not reflect what it actually costs to make the product. How do you know what it costs when you don't know what really went into it? The variance frequently gets tossed into the big slush fund—burden or overhead. Efforts to improve costs are diluted because the variances are hard to trace.

The net result? Mismanaged bill of material changes result in major financial losses. We're talking big bucks here. And most companies don't even realize it! Time and time again in our classes people who routinely handle their companies' bills don't realize the cost implications in poorly managed changes. They don't monitor change costs, and, consequently, top management isn't aware that a problem even exists. Poorly managed bill changes lead to inaccurate bills of material. This is a quality problem—the bill is not conforming to expectations. The cost of poor quality in this job—managing bill changes—is eight to 10 times higher than it should be.

Is the situation hopeless?

Not at all. Engineering changes—more accurately referred to as bill of material changes—can be handled easily and efficiently. All it takes is an effective system. In fact, this is yet another of the problems in making such changes—there's no magic involved; just basic common sense.

"Engineering" Changes?

First, let's look at the term "Engineering Changes."

Is the bill of material Engineering data? Of course not. It's company data. It's used by every portion of the company, from the shop floor to Accounting. Accordingly, changes to the bill of material don't just come from Engineering—they come from every portion of the company. Certainly the shop floor can make valuable suggestions on how a product might be improved. In fact, in many companies 50 percent or more of the bill of material changes originate from the shop floor. Everyone in the company should be able to suggest changes to the bill of material, but every change must be evaluated, documented and communicated.

Documenting each change is a major step to bringing the system under control.

Bently Nevada knows all about problems with bill of material changes. Just a few years ago, Bently Nevada had 2,000— that's right, two thousand—engineering/bill of material changes ("That's nothing," someone at Bently Nevada jokes, "The year before we had 4,000."). As Dave Biggs says, they know how to manage changes—they have no choice.

One of the first things Bently Nevada did was gather together people from all areas of the business—Production, Engineering, Marketing, Administration and Finance—and figure out just where the bill of material changes were coming from.

"The old way we used to do it," says Biggs, "was that if there was some trivial little problem on the shop floor, something that had been bugging someone for the last 10 years, that trivial thing had to go through the whole chain of command. The person would take the problem to his superior on the floor and try to convince the boss that it was important. Then they'd have to convince someone in Engineering, who couldn't care less about what happened on the shop floor. If the person convinced the engineer, then the engineer had to write up a change request, sign it off and be responsible for getting it through. We thought, `This doesn't pass the sanity test.'"

The first thing Bently Nevada did, then, was to allow Manufacturing to sign off some changes to the bill of material directly, without going through Engineering.

"Why should Engineering sign them off?" he says. "Engineering's viewpoint was that they didn't care who approved the change requests, as long as those changes didn't mess up the design. If it didn't work out, Engineering could always take Manufacturing's keys away. And it's been working great. The shop floor is probably processing 100 to 200 change requests a week."

Bently Nevada recognized an important point—all bill of material change requests are not created equal, and any formal system, to work well, has to take that fact into account.

Different Types Of Bill Changes

There are three different types of bill of material changes:
- Changes due to errors
- Mandatory changes
- Phase-ins and phase-outs

The first is bill of material changes due to errors. Bill of material accuracy is an on-going project, and sometimes there are going to be errors. Ideally, you've gone through the accuracy procedures, which include picking parts from the bill, then trying to build the product or the subassembly from the parts picked or breaking down a product and checking the parts against the bill. Any errors to the bill at this point should be quickly changed with a minimum of red tape. This includes errors discovered in the manufacturing process. As a former engineer, one of the toughest lessons I had to learn was that the bill of material was only as accurate as Manufacturing lets it be. Once an error is detected, the bill should be immediately corrected. Nothing is more frustrating to the shop floor than to have discovered an error, gone through the bill change procedures and then have the same wrong parts delivered for the next run.

> There needs to be distinctions between major and minor changes...

There also needs to be a distinction between major changes and minor changes. Obvious errors such as wrong part numbers, wrong quantity per or unit measure, no revision level, no scrap, no rework, etc., should be classified as minor and updated within 24 hours—documentation is still needed!

A second bill of material change is the mandatory change. Sometimes it's necessary to immediately change the bill of material. This can be the result of safety or liability problems, operating problems that didn't show up until the product had been out in the field for a while, a sudden shift in the market or a change in government regulations. From a paperwork point of view, this is the easiest change to make; a sort of damn the torpedoes, full speed ahead approach is called for. Erase the old parts and replace them with the new; then deal with the consequences. Old stock could be:

- Scrapped
- Reworked to the new specifications
- Used in other products
- Retained for service or repair use only

Mandatory changes are simple, but they are expensive. A

rookie engineer tells the story of his first job working for a company with a formal but complex system for bill changes. After going through the paperwork for a few changes, the disgruntled engineer asked a colleague if there wasn't an easier way to process engineering changes. Sure, the colleague, just mark the change "Mandatory" and it will slide right through. After several months of "Mandatory" changes, the engineer was invited to the office of the vice president of Manufacturing. Thinking he was in for a commendation, the engineer hurried to the appointment. After a bit of small talk, the vice president pulled out a folder and opened it up. "Now," he said, "would you like to explain why you've billed $65,000 worth of mandatory engineering changes to my budget in the last few months?"

The engineer is still employed, but is a great fan of the formal system.

The story points out three additional points in bill of material changes:

1) Changes must be classified as major or minor.

2) Every major change should be dollarized. How much is this change costing the company? How much will it save the company?

3) Every proposed change must be examined. Major changes go to the Bill of Material Review Board, made up of high level management personnel. Minor changes get handled within 24 hours, with the documentation available for review by the Bill of Material Review Board.

The Importance Of Policy

There must be a stated bill of material change policy, and there must be a bill of material change review committee to make sure that policy is being followed. The purpose of the policy is to state who can ask for a bill of material change, who can authorize such a change and how that change will be communicated to the right places throughout the company.

The bill of material change policy should identify:
• The Bill of Material Review Board members.

- Authority for approving bill of material changes.
- Conditions for new part number assignments.
- Conditions for emergency bill of material changes.
- Financial responsibility for mandatory changes.
- Responsibility for notification and follow-up on changes.

The policy needs to be written down and available to all the concerned parties. One of the best policy statements we've seen comes from APCOM in Tennessee, manufacturers of thermostats and heating elements for water heaters. Along with the policy statement, APCOM issues a worksheet to gather the specifics of the change. APCOM's 12-point engineering change policy reads like this:

APCOM's Engineering Change Policy provides for the efficient management of resources affected by an engineering change. Use of the Engineering Change Worksheet ensures good understanding of the scope of each proposed change.

1) An engineering change may be requested by any employee and routed through proper channels to Product Engineering.

2) The Engineering Change Committee consists of a representative for each of the following areas:
- Engineering (chair)
- Accounting
- Manufacturing
- Purchasing
- Marketing
- Production Control
- Bill of Material Administrator
- Alternates for each area may be assigned. Four members are to be a quorum.

3) Committee meetings are to be scheduled by the Engineering manager or his designee.

4) All changes to the bill of material, drawings, specifications or the addition of part numbers must be documented with an engineering change notice.

5) A proposed change will be assigned to an engineer, and he will be responsible for collecting data for each draft ECN.

6) An engineering change will be classified major or minor:

• A major change will require the approval of the Engineering Change Committee.

• A minor change will be presented on a draft ECN to the engineering manager or his designee to be approved, amended, tabled for further study or rejected.

The Engineering Change Worksheet will be used to define major or minor changes. However, a change indicated minor by the Engineering Change Worksheet may be deemed major by the engineer.

7) A major change will be presented at the engineering change committee meeting on a draft Engineering Change Notice. A draft may be approved, amended, tabled for further study or rejected.

8) A prerequisite to an engineering change is the completion of the Engineering Change Worksheet and the preparation of an Engineering Change Draft. Input for the Engineering Change Worksheet will be supplied by the following departments:

• Production—WIP, scrap, rework, quantity on hand.

• Production Control—quantity on hand, planning and scheduling.

• Manufacturing Engineering—Cost of new tooling, labor, cost of tooling change.

Purchasing—Availability and cost of material, quantity on hand.

Accounting—Additional cost information.

Sales and marketing—Order entry change, customer acceptance.

9) There will be one engineer designated accountable for each individual engineering change, and his name will appear on the Engineering Change Notice.

10) An engineering change that falls into any of the following categories requires approval by the president before implementation:

• An engineering change which costs APCOM in excess of $1,000.

• An engineering change which results in an increase in part costs.

• Specific items requested by the president.

11) All pertinent ECN data and visual aids will be distributed by the bill of material administrator.

12) Implementation of an engineering change is the responsibility of each department upon receipt of the issued ECN.

Notice that responsibility is clearly defined, each change is clearly documented, and no change is instituted until there is a clear understanding of all the ramifications.

> The problem with bill changes is that people don't take them seriously...

We also strongly recommend that top management be involved in the Review Board. Remember that part of the problem with bill changes is that people don't take them that seriously, which leads to a vicious snowball effect as the changes roll uncontrolled through the company. Top-level executive participation shows just how serious the company takes the changes.

Another important factor is deciding on the definition of a major change and a minor change. A minor change in one company might be one that amounts to less than $50; in another company it might be less than $1,000.

On who can authorize changes, remember Bently Nevada's example. Possibly minor changes can be authorized by Manufacturing or whatever department the change requests come from. This streamlines the process as much as possible while retaining accountability.

The change review committee accepts or rejects the requests for major changes from the B/M Administrator, then determines the disposition of the change notice. The change notice is distributed, the change itself is implemented, then everyone involved is notified.

Phase-In And Phase-Out

The next type of bill of material change is the phase-in of one component and the phase-out of another. This is the least costly type of change, but, paradoxically, it's the hardest to control. Volatile manufacturing schedules, scrapping work-in-process and untimely inventory adjustments make this type of change difficult to manage. Economically balancing out existing inventory, avoiding delays in using new items and not yet running out of the old items before the new ones are available is a neat trick if you can do it.

As we move more toward a JIT environment, with less and less WIP, it does become easier to phase in a new product, since there's never much WIP or inventory to deal with. The short lead times help, but you still need to carefully plan when the new product will become available.

MRP II, of course, will continue planning the old item unless the bill of material is changed. The trick is to predict in advance the stockout date of the old part and schedule the new one to arrive at the precise time it's needed.

MRP II can help us here. There are three techniques used to phase in one component and phase out the other. The first and simplest method is making the new part a component of the old part. (Figure 1)

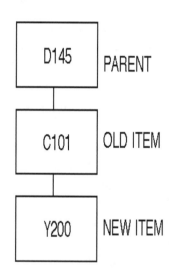

Figure 1: Method 1

In this case, the new part (Y200) is made a component of the old part (C101). The lead time for the old part is set to zero and the order quantity lot-to-lot. When the quantity of C101 reaches zero, MRP II blows through C101 to the component and begins planning and scheduling Y200.

This is a super simple method, but it must be used cautiously and not used at all in many cases, as it has some disadvantages.

Bills of material are supposed to show the way a product is built. Suppose C101 is a casting; Y200 is also a casting. That means we have a casting being made from a casting. An engineer not familiar with the substitution might completely eliminate Y200, thinking it was a mistake.

This system also makes it hard to do a proper cost roll-up. In fact, if you did a roll-up of A935, you'd get a double cost on that component. An alternative is to show a zero cost for one of the components, but that isn't a good accounting procedure.

This method can't be used where a component is being replaced in some, but not all, usage. This technique assumes all requirements for the old part number should be passed on to the new part number. Finally, this method can only be used for a simple one-on-one replacement. In a more complicated replacement, such as a situation where three components in an assembly are being replaced simultaneously by three other components, it's difficult to make the method work.

To even try to make it work would necessitate structuring a bill of material so all three new components are tied to the item you want to use up. This just compounds the confusion in the Engineering Department (not to mention any people outside Engineering) and the costing problems. If it's confusing to have a casting made from a casting, think of a situation where a casting, a cardboard box and an O-ring are made from a casting!

A second technique is the use of the effectivity date, or

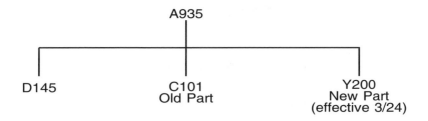

BILL OF MATERIAL FILE

Parent	Component	Effective Date	End or Start Code
A935	D145		
A935	C101	3/24	E
A935	Y200	3/24	S

Figure 2: Effectivity Dates

effective serial number or lot number. The effectivity date is created by adding a special field in the bill of material file. The date in that field is coded as being either a beginning or an ending date. (See Figure 2, previous page) Both the old and the new parts are stored in the bill of material record, and when the computer accesses the bill of material, it selects the correct components as of a given date, serial number or lot number.

This is a very logical way of approaching phase-in and phase-out. The biggest problem is that it doesn't take into account the realities of the manufacturing situation. The actual effectivity date is generally a moving target.

Go back to the example of phasing out the C101 and phasing in the Y200. The date of the phase-out is 3/24, the date when all the old components will be used up. Suppose, though, the master production schedule is changed and the planned orders for A935 which were later than 3/24 are now earlier than 3/24. Instead of exploding to generate requirements for Y200, the new parts, the planned orders now create requirements for the old parts. The planner orders more old parts, completely demolishing the carefully planned phase-in and phase-out.

If the requirement for the old part changes, there's scrap, or any of a long list of things happen, the effectivity date changes, meaning that someone must be constantly monitoring that date. Again, the more complicated the routine, the less likely it is to be maintained.

An FPO Solution

The most flexible and practical way for dealing with phase-out and phase-in is the firm planned order method. Basically, the firm planned order method expands on the planning and scheduling capabilities of material requirements planning to handle the phase-in and phase-out.

For example, X309, X310 and X311 are simultaneously replacing C444, B305 and R970 on parent item A935. The objective is to make enough A935's out of the old parts until they are used up and then start making A935's out of the new parts. Of course we don't live in a perfect world; therefore the inventory of old parts is not in perfect balance. The planner determines the quantity of A935's to firm plan that will use up most of the old parts, thus minimizing the volume of obsolete parts to scrap. The controlling part is the one with the largest inventory(in dollars). In this case B305.

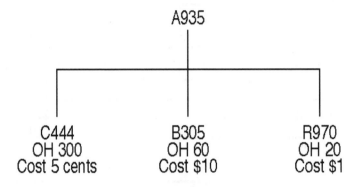

Figure 3: The Controlling Part

A bill of material is generated, tied to a firm planned order and placed in the Requirements File. Once in the Requirements File, the bill of material is frozen and can be altered as necessary by the planner. The planner replaces the old parts in the Master Bill of Material file with the new parts.

REQUIREMENTS FILE		BILL OF MATERIAL FILE	
Part No.	Qty.	Part No.	Qty.
C444	60	X309	1
B305	60	X310	1
R970	60	X311	1

Figure 4: The Requirements File

Prior to making the change to the bill of material file the material plan for B305 (old part) and X310 (new part it replaces) looked like :

A935

LT: 2   OQ: 75

		Period							
		1	2	3	4	5	6	7	8
Projected Reqts.		10	20	35	15	40	25	10	55
Scheduled Reqts.									
On-Hand	150	140	120	85	70	30	5	-5	-60
Planned Order Release						75			75

B305

LT: 2   OQ: 100

		Period							
		1	2	3	4	5	6	7	8
Projected Reqts.						75			75
Scheduled Reqts.									
On-Hand	60	60	60	60	60	-15	-15	-15	-90
Planned Order Release				100					

X310

LT: 2   OQ: 100

		Period							
		1	2	3	4	5	6	7	8
Projected Reqts.									
Scheduled Reqts.									
On-Hand	0	0	0	0	0	0	0	0	0
Planned Order Release									

Figure 5: Pre-Change Material Plan

After making the changes to the Requirements and bill of material files the material plan for these parts looks like Figure 6, next page.

Material requirements planning will plan and schedule enough of the old parts for that firm planned order regardless of whether the order has to be rescheduled forward or backward in time. Material requirements planning will plan and schedule the new parts without affecting the firm planned order and automatically adjust the phase-in timing when the master schedule changes.

If any changes occur, material requirements planning will flag the firmed planned order to be rescheduled. When the start date is changed, the requirements for the old parts will be changed.

A935
LT: 2   OQ: 75

		Period							
		1	2	3	4	5	6	7	8
Projected Reqts.		10	20	35	15	40	25	10	55
Scheduled Reqts.									
On-Hand	150	140	120	85	70	30	5	-5	-60
Planned Order Release						60			75

B305
LT: 2   OQ: 1

		Period							
		1	2	3	4	5	6	7	8
Projected Reqts.						60			0
Scheduled Reqts.						60			
On-Hand	60	60	60	60	60	0	0	0	0
Planned Order Release									

X310
LT: 2   OQ: 100

		Period							
		1	2	3	4	5	6	7	8
Projected Reqts.									75
Scheduled Reqts.									
On-Hand	0	0	0	0	0	0	0	0	-75
Planned Order Release							100		

Figure 6: The New Plan

Material requirements planning automatically changes the planned orders, which will cause the requirements for the new parts to be changed. The schedule to phase out the old part and phase in the new parts is automatically maintained with routine responses by the planner. The order policy on the old parts should be changed to lot-to-lot if the old part is to be phased out entirely. This will avoid ordering a full lot size when only a smaller quantity is needed to balance out the old inventory.

Obviously, to use this method, your system needs to be able to create a Requirements File. That file can be created automatically, but never regenerated automatically. Changes to the file must be manually originated. In addition, the pick list or material requisitions for manufacturing orders must be printed from the Requirements File, not from the bill of material file.

Discussion Points

1. Estimate or measure the number of bill of material changes that occur annually in your company. What business problems does this volume of bill of material changes cause?

2. Identify problems in your company caused by not effectively managing bill of material changes. Estimate the financial cost and other negative impacts on your business.

3. Discuss and define the scope in your business of the term "making bill of material changes." What does this really mean?

4. Discuss the three types of bill of material changes. Which ones are more prevalent in your company? Please discuss.

5. Discuss the elements of a good bill of material change policy and how they apply to your company.

6. How are bill of material changes classified as major or minor in your company? Are they handled differently? If so, how?

7. Discuss the problems caused by using the phase-in and phase-out approach to implementing bill of material changes. Estimate the financial and other negative impacts in your business when this approach is not effectively used.

8. Discuss potential problems with assigning effectivity dates (or effectivity serial or lot numbers) to implementing bill of material changes.

9. Using an example from your business, discuss how the Firm Planned Order approach to implementing bill of material changes could be used in your company.

10. Identify and discuss the advantages of using the Firm Planned Order approach to implementing bill of material changes.

Chapter 15

New Product Introductions

Product quality has become a given, almost a commodity. Defect-free products aren't enough to differentiate a company from the competition and lead the industry. Squeezing costs out of "me too" products will soon drive the business into the commodity arena where it gets tougher to make a buck. The alternative is to innovate. Offer something different and do it often. This means faster product development times and shorter product life cycles.

Traditionally, new product development suffered from the silo effect. This critical business process was viewed as an engineering responsibility, isolated in the engineering silo. The product would eventually be "released" to manufacturing. Documentation, including bills of material, specs, and drawings would be lobbed over the engineering silo wall into the manufacturing silo. Manufacturing and purchasing would begin the process of deciding how and if the product could be produced.

The results of this approach were poor at best. Manufacturing costs were excessive and exceeded target. Bills of material were incomplete, inaccurate and didn't reflect the way the product had to be produced. All of these mistakes had to be corrected while trying to scale up production. The products went to market late and often how to be recalled or fixed in the field. The formal bill material system was quickly swamped under a tidal wave of changes after release. Obsolete inventory of the old product piled up in warehouses. And these are only a few of the symptoms of poor quality in the new product development processes.

Bently Nevada suffered through many of these same symptoms until they developed and implemented MAP (Market Aimed Products). MAP is a formal, well-defined—and revolutionary—process for developing new products.

MAP PROCESS
Phases & Gates

Figure 1: The MAP Process

Simultaneously designing the business processes and the product is one of the critical principles of MAP. An essential component of the business process is creating and maintaining a well defined bill of material. Formal documentation and control of the bill of material has been viewed as an activity only applicable after the product has been "released " to manufacturing. In MAP language this is during the launch phase. The problem with this thinking is that many of the internal customers never see the bill and use it until the eleventh hour. Among the rationales are "too many changes will occur during design", " too much red tape to document the changes", "it will take too long to put the data into the system" and many more. If we can control bill of material changes for a mature product, why can't we control changes for new product? We can. It does require a major paradigm shift in how we view managing bills of material for new products during the design phase.

Controlling An Introduction

The first step in managing a new product launch is to see that the new product is integrated into the formal planning and scheduling system. After all, isn't a new product just a mature product who's bills have gone through a bunch of additions, deletions or changes? If adds, deletes and changes for mature products can be managed through the formal system, so can a new products.

Let's first look at the way a typical new product is typically designed. The first step is research and development, creating a breadboard model or a prototype. This is the sort of the raw engineering stage, where changes happen to the new product on a daily basis. The next stage is the design prototype—the new product is beginning to take shape.

After the design prototype, we move to the production prototype. This is the new product as it will be made in production. Then we transition into the initial production run. After a while—including a period of design changes based on customer feedback—we have a mature product. Engineering incubates the new product until the initial production run, when it becomes Manufacturing's baby.

Typically, Manufacturing would like these phases done in a series, i.e., first the design prototype until all of the bugs are worked out. Then pass the product to manufacturing and give them plenty of time to make the production prototype. In the real world, this is a dream—it simply takes too long, which means the possibility of missing the market. The reality is that the development processes must overlap—materials for the production run will probably be ordered before the design prototype is finished. And we want customer feedback as early as possible. All this means many "different" products being made simultaneously. That means lots of clear communications are absolutely necessary—the left hand must know what the right hand is doing!

While engineering is designing the product manufacturing needs to be "test driving" the new product, evaluating manufacturability at the point changes can still be made economically.

Our goal should be to move into the manufacturing phase with no expediting, meeting Marketing's delivery guarantees, all at minimum costs. Management will be pushing hard, because the first four stages are a financial drain on the company with nothing coming back until the production lines are running.

Two questions here:

1) How do we use the bill of material to ease the birthing pains, and

2) At what point does the formal system kick in?

> How do we use the bill of material to ease the birthing pains...

Here's a radical idea: The formal system, including a new bill of material, should begin right along with the initial breadboard model. As the bills are loaded into the computer file, they can be used to order and schedule all materials needed to make the prototype and initial production runs.

At the beginning, you only need two part numbers—one for the finished new product and the other for the first item identified by the engineer to be used in the new product. You don't need a complete bill of material to start planning a new product. The bill of material can evolve right alongside the product.

Since each phase—breadboard model, design prototype, production prototype, initial production run—is usually significantly different, a different parent part number can be used to uniquely identify and schedule that product.

At the very first stage, breadboarding or toolroom prototyping, there's likely going to be a need for components or raw materials to build the new product. If there are several components or raw materials going into the new product, it's not likely that all the raw materials and components have the same lead time to acquire. A very basic bill of material can be drawn up, and Production Planning can get to work planning and scheduling the parts

Engineering knows are needed for the breadboarding or prototyping.

As the product evolves, so does the bill of material. Dummy part numbers can be loaded into the bill for subassemblies you expect to use but don't yet know the full configuration. For example, if the new product will have a frame assembly, but you don't know exactly what it will look like at the beginning, give the frame assembly a dummy number. If you know some of the parts that will go into the frame assembly, then include them on the bill of material for the dummy frame assembly.

As more parts for the frame assembly become known, add them to the bill of material. When you've finalized the frame assembly, go into the system, delete the dummy part number and replace it with the real part number.

All of this is easier said than done. On a psychological level, it sort of goes against the grain of the way Engineering departments like to work. One thing we've heard time and again is that a formal system like the one described, "cuts into Engineering's creativity." A formal system instituted in the early stages of product development is perceived as cutting into the freewheeling give-and-take of Engineering development.

They have a legitimate point. At the earliest stages of product development, Engineering needs a very free hand. That, however, can be incorporated into the formal system. The normal bill of material change procedures need to be modified for the new product development stage. One of the best ways of handling this is allowing the Product Development Engineer to have the responsibility for engineering changes at this stage. In effect, the engineer becomes the Bill of Material Review Board and assumes those responsibilities.

> The normal B/M change procedures need to be modified for the new product development stage...

This system has the added benefit of thoroughly documenting the changes a product goes through during development, a function as helpful to Engineering as to Manufacturing. Another advantage to using the formal system early on is that MRP II can begin planning and scheduling the needed materials immediately, and include an automatic notice of open purchase orders or manufacturing orders that need to be canceled for items that have been designed out of the prototype. This helps prevent obsolete inventory.

Using The Bill To Smooth The Edges

Why not use the bill of material to plan and schedule all the items necessary for a new product introduction?

Ideally, the bill of material for the new product should contain more than just the raw materials and components that go into the new product. The tooling for the new product, if it is different from existing tooling, should definitely be included on the bill. The same goes for items such as catalog pages describing the new product or spec sheets. In fact, the bill should include all the items or activities necessary to get the new product out the front door. It doesn't matter whether we can't ship a new truck because the engine isn't available or the instruction manual isn't ready—the truck still can't go out the door, and we still can't get paid for it.

By learning the lead time for each section of the bill, we can realistically assess how the new product introduction is going. For example, because of a long lead time at the catalog printer, a sample of the real new product might not be available in time, and we might have to create a dummy product for the catalog photo.

Competing in today's global market means getting new, innovative products to the market before the competition. By using the formal system during the early engineering stages, all of the documentation necessary to get into production is being "tested," checked out for clarity, etc., in parallel with the actual product being tested. Too often, the new product is fully designed and ready to go when we discover the production people really don't understand what they're supposed to do. An early "test run" can translate into avoiding costly delays in new product introductions.

New Product Development Checklist

We've created a New Product System Checklist to make new product development as painless as possible. Your system should be able to:

1) Handle partial bill of material releases.

2) Handle many bill of material changes.

3) Allow streamlined bill of material change approvals.

4) Be able to quickly communicate shop/purchase schedule changes. Although this doesn't guarantee there will be no shortages or excesses, it does allow quick communication of potential problems.

5) Be able to monitor the introduction schedule.

- Is it on time? Are all materials on schedule?
- Is it ahead of time? Are materials already here and available? Should we consider introducing the product sooner?
- Is it behind schedule? Should we consider delaying the release?
- There should be at least weekly new product meetings of all the parties involved to make sure the program is on track.

6) Monitor projected obsolete inventory.

7) Use the MRP II firmed planned order technique described in "Changes to the Bill of Material" chapter for accurate and smooth introductions.

8) Schedule non-product-related items.
- Drawings
- Tooling
- Routing
- Supplies

9) Plan capacity requirements.

If the new product is to be phased in and an old product phased out, the problem is to decide when the inventory of the old product will be sufficiently balanced to minimize obsolescence costs before shifting to the new product. MRP II can help, but it can't make the final decision. A human hand needs to be at the helm.

The procedure is the one we outlined in the previous chapter on phasing in and phasing out parts. Due to variance in lot sizes, variations in lead times and scrap, the inventory will never be in perfect balance. The first step is to try to minimize the excess inventory on the most expensive items and order just enough of the others to balance out. Next, master schedule just enough of the old product to exhaust the inventory on the controlling items. Assign a new part number to the new or redesigned product. The master schedule for the new product should pick up where the master schedule for the old product left off. Some overlap should be planned in case the new product isn't ready on schedule. Gross requirements for the old parts should be zero beyond the time period when the new product takes over. The new products will be planned in time for the switchover. Gross requirements for the parts used in both the old and new products will be scheduled to be available for either design.

Bently Nevada, because it manufactures electronic equipment for a changing market, has anywhere from one new product a month to one new product a week. Part of the push to get control of its new product design came from the marketplace—while Bently Nevada was working on an overhaul of a major product line, several new competitors jumped into the field to fill that particular niche.

"Had we been more efficient," says Ray Bacon, "our competitors would not have had that niche to come into."

Before MAP Bently Nevada engineers described new product development as "a cross between a Chinese fire drill and World War III..."

The biggest problem was that Manufacturing couldn't build the product Engineering designed—at least, not the way Engineering designed it. Engineering pointed out that it didn't have any trouble building a prototype; Manufacturing countered by stating that Engineering had to build only one. The problem was the bill of material, which was getting put together more as an afterthought than as part of the process.

Now, Bently Nevada starts the bill of material creation and

processing at the earliest design phase, being careful not to create a product or a bill of material that is going to cause trouble when it moves to the manufacturing stage. In fact, before the product "is thrown over the fence" to Production, an engineer builds what Bently Nevada terms the "first article." This is, in effect, the production prototype. It is built strictly from the bill of material, using routings and drawings that are included in the bill.

"The tendency in the past," says a Bently Nevada engineer, "was to allow Engineering to build the first article using their schematics and their own bill of material. It took a lot of browbeating to get a technician to build from the real bill of material."

The result is that the documentation will be correct; the bill of material will be accurate.

"We may find that the order in which we do things is out of whack with the way Production wants to do things," the engineer says. "At least the right parts are there, which is a major step in the right direction."

Discussion Points

1. When are bills of material created for new products in your company? Discuss any problems this approach may cause.

2. Discuss typical bill of material problems for new products.

3. Discuss potential advantages if component parts or items are ordered using a bill of material that was created during product development and before the new products are released from Engineering.

4. Discuss problems that might be encountered by creating and using bills of material during new product development and prior to Engineering release. Discuss solutions.

5. Discuss the significance and meaning of the nine items listed in this chapter that your new product system should be capable of handling.

Making The Changes

Changing a manufacturing process isn't really the hardest thing in the world. Changing people is the hardest thing in the world. The biggest obstacle to changing the bill of material isn't the part number question or how to modularize the bill, it's making the people equation work. There are substantial problems in our way.

The first is, "We've always done it that way, and it's always worked." Every company we've worked with, with the exception of new companies, has had to deal with this problem. So will you.

The second problem you'll hear goes something like, "Restructuring the bill is a great idea. Get on it right after lunch and wrap it up before Friday." Too many times people are looking for a quick fix, sort of a bill of material restructuring pill that works faster than aspirin and lasts longer than the average cold.

A third people problem is the dreaded pointed finger "That's your job, your responsibility. Change the bill and let us know what we have to do." Of course, restructuring the bill is everybody's job.

Even a small manufacturing plant sometimes more resembles a group of squabbling small nations than a single company working together to satisfy the customer and make money for everyone. We go into companies that are so at each other's throats that "today's war is posted on the bulletin board up front; Today, it's Accounting versus Manufacturing. Tomorrow, it's Engineering versus Quality Assurance. Friday, MIS takes on all comers.

We all laugh, but it's laughter tinged with a hint of embarrassment. We've all been there.

The greatest strength of the Japanese is not their automation or their manufacturing structures. It's their recognition that the "enemy" is outside the company, not inside. They recognize that teamwork and cooperation are necessary to survive and prosper in a world manufacturing environment. They recognize that the time and energy necessary to maintain Shop Wars are time and money taken away from the central purpose of manufacturing, to fill a need.

Restructuring the bill of material can help a company meet that objective. I can also help solidify the teamwork concept and help give the company a sense of purpose.

You'll notice that some of the companies we've mentioned throughout this book didn't necessarily succeed in restructuring the bill of material the first time out. APCOM, for example, hammered away at it a couple of times before everything came together. You'll also notice that the companies that have gone through a restructuring on their way to "Class A" performance have received substantial benefits from their work.

Over the next few chapters we'll be looking at some of the people problems and solutions involved in a bill restructuring. We'll also touch on hardware and software, two frequent stumbling blocks on the path to good manufacturing techniques.

Chapter 16

Introduction To Implementing Change

Who is responsible for bill of material changes?

We have seen that everyone in the plant has a legitimate need for the bill. Engineering creates the original bill of material; Production uses the bill to build the product; Planning and Scheduling uses the bill to determine which parts need to be available when; Purchasing uses the bill to determine what items to buy; Finance uses the bill to calculate product cost. There are many users, but who should be in charge of the restructuring?

The answer is, of course, everyone who has a stake in the bill, which translates into the whole company team. One of our basic tenets, though, is to never show anyone the solution to a problem when he or she doesn't understand the problem in the first place.

Very likely, bill of material restructuring is part of (or is going to be part of) the implementation of MRP II, JIT, TQM or a similar process. We have found that this implementation of any new system virtually requires that the people involved know both what's at stake and what stands to be gained by successful implementation and restructuring of the bill of material.

In the successful companies we've profiled throughout the book, there are certain common denominators. One of those common denominators is the willingness of the companies to try innovative strategies to break down the artificial barriers within the company.

At Bently Nevada, company founder Don Bently decided to get serious about MRP II after an IBM seminar. The first tries to implement the program failed, Dave Biggs remembers.

> "I had been trained as an engineer and didn't have the slightest idea what manufacturing was..."

"I was in Engineering," Biggs says. "Had been trained to be an engineer and didn't have the slightest idea what manufacturing was. Don (Bently) and Roger (Harker) called me down to the office one day and said, `Dave, we want you to run the MRP II project in manufacturing.'

"I said, `Gee whiz, wait a minute. I don't understand Manufacturing. I kind of like Engineering. I'm doing a good job over there. I don't even know what MRP II is!'" Biggs continues. "And Don said, `Let me restate the question.' The next Monday morning I was project manager."

The advantage was that, for the first time, Engineering and Manufacturing got together on a single project, the implementation of MRP II.

"Basically, there is a challenge," says Dave Biggs. "And we still struggle with the bill of material. Bill of material generation, product structuring, is a very difficult process. It's not a process that you can learn, get the formula down pat and just say, `Boy, I got that one,' and just walk away. It's a continuing learning process. Every time you bring out a new product, you use your past experience and your future idea to see if you can do it better. We've evolved to the point where we want to make sure the bill of material does the job for Manufacturing, does the job for

Engineering, does the job for the sales people...On this journey, every time we do a new product, we're challenged to figure out how we're going to structure the product and the bill of material. How do we make it easy to order? How do we make it easy to service? How do we make sure the bill of material accurately reflects the way we build the product?"

Different Responsibilities

Every part of the company has responsibilities in handling the bill of material. Every department is part of the bill of material process; they're all internal customers and suppliers. It's up to Engineering to provide the list of components and subassemblies, plus all the appropriate specifications.

Manufacturing adds manufacturing subassemblies, semi-finished parts and raw materials and supplies.

Planning and Scheduling, along with Sales and Marketing, works on the planning bill and provides the correct percentages.

At the focus of all this activity is the Bill of Material Administrator, who is responsible for editing the input and maintaining the quality of the bill of material file. The B/M Administrator also coordinates changes to the bill and notification to other departments when the bill is changed.

Here's an example of a job description for the B/M Administrator, this one from APCOM:

Bill of Material Change Control: Keeping the bill of material up to date is the primary responsibility of the B/M Administrator. He acts as the center of control regarding all transactions to the bill of material. Difficulties regarding any of his job duties must be reported to the Engineering Manager.

The B/M Administrator will prepare an ECN draft with the information furnished by the product engineer assigned to the particular product. The B/M Administrator will attend the Engineering Change Committee meetings as an observer. All drawings, process data and all other pertinent data is to be released with the approved ECN.

Product Engineering Data Entry: The approved ECN draft

is authorization for the B/M Administrator to initiate the part number entry per the Engineering Change Notice. All product engineering data entry will be completed before the release of the ECN.

Bill of Material Accuracy: The first workday of each week, the B/M Administrator will publish a list of bills of material to be audited that week. B/Ms for audit will be selected by: 1) recent B/M additions, 2) recent B/M changes, 3) suspect B/Ms reported to the B/M Administrator and 4) random selection.

> Every part of the company has responsibilities in handling the bill...

The B/M Administrator will use the audit documentation furnished by the product engineer and the production foreman to prepare graphs to show the percentage of accuracy of all B/Ms audited. It will be his responsibility to keep all documentation on file in an orderly fashion. A report to the Engineering Manager and Master Scheduling Review Committee will be made on a weekly basis as to the B/M accuracy.

Engineering Change Follow-Up: Phase-in/phase-out changes will require close communications between Planners and the B/M Administrator to assure that B/M changes will allow adequate planning of materials. The B/M Administrator will be responsible for delivering copies of the changed B/Ms to the production departments and picking up all obsolete B/Ms and destroying them.

The B/M Administrator

B/M Administrators have typically reported to Engineering (as in the case of APCOM). That isn't, though, written in stone. Lately, we've seen a trend to have the B/M Administrator report to the head of Manufacturing. The important fact is that having a B/M Administrator signifies that the company is serious about bill of material accuracy. The B/M Administrator is also important because he or she provides a focal point for bill accuracy measurements, bill changes and new bill of material structuring. Within the context of the organization, a B/M Administrator is a good idea because it takes the responsibility for the day-to-day maintenance of the bill out of what are probably already overworked Engineering and Manufacturing departments. It helps keep the bill from becoming a political football within the company— remember, we're trying to build a company database here, not fall back into the outmoded habits of parochialism.

We want to adhere to the bill of material structuring principles:

- Satisfy *all* users.
- *Shallow* as possible.
- *Unique* part numbers.
- Include *all* scheduled items.
- Identify *material*, not labor.
- Contain *part number*, not drawing number.
- All parts *additive*.
- Changes approved *before* notification.

Steps For Restructuring A Bill

Keeping those eight points in mind, let's look at the steps to take for a bill of material restructuring:

1) Educate bill of material users in the basic principles. This usually means the project leader and several key bill of material users need to attend a class or classes outside the company.

2) Form the bill of material project team.

3) Educate more people in the basics, using classes inside the company conducted by project team members.

4) Define item and bill of material data.

5) Establish a bill of material administration group.

6) Load the bill of material by product.

7) Use the new bill of material to build products.

8) Measure bill of material accuracy.

One point that companies continually mention is the need for education. The first need is for outside education. In fact, the two most frequent mistakes in implementing a change in bill of material structure are doing little or no education or failing to do the education entirely. They jump to Step Six—Load the bill of material—and later they end up adding Step Nine—Re-restructure and reload!

We have an odd relationship with education. Too often, we see education as something we did in high school, college, graduate school, which basically is learn facts, pass test and move on, not worrying whether you can remember anything. A popular comedian refers to the "Five-Minute University," where you just learn the things that you're not going to forget anyway. Or we see continuing education as purely a function of working in a technical field. An engineer is expected to keep current on technical changes. Pilots might need to return to flight school to keep their skills current. Teachers need refresher courses to keep their teaching certificates. Even mechanics must go back to school to learn how to repair this year's model automobile.

Outside education helps prevent the "Reinventing the Wheel" Syndrome...

But management systems, ways to run the business? Isn't that something that you just pick up on?

No, it's not.

The last few years of competing in a world marketplace have taught us that. No one in Detroit laughs at Japanese management systems anymore. We need to learn how to change the way we run our businesses, and outside education is a jump start for that process.

Outside education also helps to head off the "Reinventing The Wheel" syndrome. As we mentioned earlier, most manufacturing businesses have much more in common than their managers imagine. Constantly, in our classes, we see the light of recognition in the participants' eyes when they hear exactly the same problem described by someone in an industry that bears not the slightest resemblance to their industry. It *is* a shock for someone in the business of making battle tanks to discover that he or she has many of the same problems as the ladies' hosiery industry. The important thing to realize is that if the problems are the same, so are many of the solutions. There's no need for manufacturing companies to spend critical resources reinventing solutions that have existed for years.

Outside education brings together people from many industries in a setting that allows them to not only share their own solutions, but have those solutions put into perspective by an experienced teacher.

There's also a sense that only certain people need education. Obviously, the B/M Administrator is going to need education. But what about the shop floor foremen? A lot of responsibility for catching any glitches in the bills is going to be put on their shoulders. In fact, the question is not who should be educated, but rather who can the company afford *not* to educate?

Centrilift sent out a regular newsletter during its bill of material restructuring. That newsletter covered the function of the bill of material, the concept of a modularizing bills, what was involved in the implementation of the new structure and then an update on what was to be accomplished in the future. Aside from the fact that such a newsletter is an excellent idea and an important communication tool, the parting comments are telling:

"We said we were going to change our system of running the business, and we are...together. As you've seen, even just one phase of the project is not always easy to accomplish, but *we are making progress and it shows.*"

Discussion Points

1. Who is responsible and accountable for structuring bills of material in your company today? Discuss any problems this current organizational approach creates.

2. Discuss the role of different functional areas in providing input to properly structuring bills of material.

3. List and discuss the responsibility of a Bill of Material Administrator.

4. Discuss the meaning in your business of each of the eight bill of material structuring principles identified in this chapter.

5. Discuss how you accomplish each of the eight steps in structuring the bill of material.

6. Discuss the importance of developing a common understanding and consensus of bill of material structuring with an effective education program.

7. Discuss the consequences if you don't have this common understanding and consensus.

8. Discuss how an effective bill of material education program will be accomplished in your company. Identify specific action steps.

9. Identify who should be included in your bill of material education programs.

Chapter 17

Hardware, Software and "People"-ware

We all love surprises, don't we? Christmas, birthdays, surprise parties—all fun and surprises. There's one area, though, that we can all live without, and that's computer hardware and software surprises.

Of course, that's an area where we always seem to get surprised. In the course of preparing this book, we heard enough computer horror stories to ice a CEO's heart. Hundreds of thousands of dollars spent for hardware or software that didn't meet company needs or required extensive—and expensive—customization to work with a semblance of what had been expected. In fact, there seems to be a pattern to it:

- Get computer.
- Get software.
- Get disappointed.
- Get new software.
- Get larger computer.
- Get frustrated.
- Get another job...

Is this because all computer sales people are thieves and liars?

Of course not.

Computers and software can certainly be effective tools to help a company become more competitive. But the goal should not be to simply computerize or automate. Unfortunately, many companies still have not seemed to have gotten this message.

> Never give someone the answer to a problem if they don't understand the problem...

"APCOM wanted to get involved with a computer to provide services for the company," says the person who became the bill restructuring team leader. "George Fuhrman, the president and CEO of the company had said that the only way we were going to get a computer was if it provided some functions for the production end. Accounting wanted the computer, but the president—rightly—wouldn't let them have it unless it could deal with...the bills of material, the routing, things like that."

Obviously, CEO Fuhrman was one company head who already knew the basics of bringing a company on-line. APCOM purchased a computer and software, hired a full-time data processing person, then hired a specialist to "maintain" what was supposed to be a functioning Accounting and Production control system.

"Low and behold, we were deceived," says the project team leader, laughing now. He spent six months trying to keep the system running. By the end of 1980, APCOM threw in the towel and opted for a new system. The project team leader looked at enhancements in hardware and enhancements in software and was trying to make the decision when he came across a brochure for a five-day class in Atlanta to learn about implementing MRP II.

"Our CEO saw the light," the team leader says ruefully.

The light is that hardware and software are secondary to "people"-ware. We frequently see implementation programs that focus on installing this module or software or that module or software. That's a dead giveaway that the people doing the installing don't really understand what it takes to become more competitive. They often misunderstand planning and scheduling and see it as a production control issue, not a companywide problem.

Before beginning to install computers and software packages, the key managers in the company should first understand what the problems are and what the strategy is to solve those problems—*never give someone the answer to a problem if he or she doesn't understand the problem!*

In the case of the bill of material, if everyone in the company thinks the informal system works just fine and that anyone who'd want to change such a good system must be crazy from the heat, you've got your work cut out for you. Before you even think about the computer package, you need a companywide education plan to explain what you're doing and why.

In implementing a production control system and revamping the bills of material, we have two initial behavioral things going against us—the "Quick Fix" mentality and a severe case of gadget fever. The first, and largest, is the "Quick Fix" mentality. TV dinners and microwave ovens have prospered because of the undeniable appeal of the quick fix. How many times have you seen people jump at a quick and dirty solution to a business problem? We're all probably guilty, at one time or another, of latching onto an apparently painless panacea to overcome problems and frustrations.

> Before you can even think about the computer package, you need a company education plan...

MRP II is a frequent victim of the quick fix mentality. Some people think MRP II stands for "Miracle Requirements Planning." Others believe JIT is a program where the vendors keep the inventory. TQC is an SPC chart, and on and on. That applies to revamping the bill of material structure as well. A company might buy a software package, turn it over to the Data Processing and wait for all the bill of material problems to start sorting themselves out. Operations people don't understand the system and don't use it. The shop floor shrugs it off as another management boondoggle. The computer hardware and software is installed and running, but no one uses it. People at *all* levels in the organization are not educated or prepared for the significant changes in the way the business is being run. Their fears, misunderstandings and lack of confidence result in resistance.

> Too often, we see the gadget as the solution to the problem...

Too often, we see the gadget as the solution to the problem, not the tool to be used for solving the problem. It is a lot easier to buy hardware and software than to successfully change behavior.

Of course, when it doesn't work, it all gets blamed on the computer system. A couple of people in Data Processing are sacrificed, a new software package is purchased, and the whole thing starts over again.

In evaluating hundreds of software packages over the years, we've isolated three basic reasons why those "computer solutions" fail:

1) *Company's expectations of the software packages significantly exceed the packages' capability.* While customizing and modifying software packages should be minimized, enhancements are usually inevitable. Writing programs to interface with existing systems is often required. Some features may be necessary for one company but not for another, which is logical, since it's impractical for the software packages to have every feature every company needs available. Many companies purchased a software package and were simply not prepared to bring the software capabilities up to match their needs.

2) *Shortcomings in software packages are discovered too late.* This is the "Surprise!" syndrome. MRP II software packages have been around since 1969. After that many years of experience, one might expect the packages to be functionally complete. They aren't. There are tools mentioned in this book, such as the Requirements File and the lead time offset, phantom logic and the

point-of-use tie-in, that are not available or are available in a different form in some packages. If missing items aren't discovered until deep into the implementation process, you can expect lengthy delays while programmers fill in the blanks.

3) *Inadequate support from Systems and Data Processing.* Competent Systems/Data Processing personnel are a critical resource, especially when the software is not complete. When enhancements or modifications to software packages are required, people with a sense of urgency and a track record of getting the job done are essential. There are education and behavioral questions here as well. Sometimes programmers doesn't really understand the user's needs. This typically happens in companies where time isn't spent educating Data Processing people as well as users.

In bill of material restructuring, the "Quick Fix" is to use a software package to maintain the bill. Software is inherently limited by its narrow focus. The bill is company data that links with many other business management functions. Unless those linkages are provided, you don't get the full benefits restructuring the bills of material.

Secondly, a software package does nothing to address the critical issues of if and when to modularize the bill. Software approaches bills of material in the most basic way, a bill of material for each end item. For companies with a large number of items, that's simply not a viable approach. A modularized bill is far more intelligent.

Probably any package can be made to work, and any hardware can be utilized. There are small companies maintaining their bills on personal computers.

The hardware and software is secondary to a companywide understanding of what you're trying to do!

The Importance Of Understanding

There are important points to consider about software. The most important piece of advice is the same as the advice on the bill itself—simplify.

1) *Educate before selecting a package.* Don't put the software cart before the MRP II, JIT or TQC horse. Be sure a critical mass of users representing all departments have a thorough understanding of why we need a new system and how to apply the concepts to their various departments before selecting the software package. First, define the needs of the business; then, compare the packages and see how they meet those requirements.

2) *Seek simple software.* Beware of gadget fever. Complexity in software doesn't necessarily mean the software is functionally complete. Avoid packages that are loaded down with too many bells and whistles. For example, one package requires five elements that must be determined for every part for calculating lead time to offset planned orders! Complex software is not only more costly, but more difficult to maintain.

3) *Insist on standard features.* The logic and content of output reports needed for "Class A" MRP II are very standard and clearly defined. Make sure the software package meets these simple minimum standards.

4) *Don't procrastinate.* If MRP II can save the company one million dollars a month, any six-month implementation delay will cost the company six million dollars! Procrastinating about software can quickly become the major cost of software.

Software Checklist

There's a checklist for bill of material software that includes:

1) Mandatory data fields. Those fields include parent/component number and quantity per.

2) Flexibility to add additional data fields, such as the find (or balloon) number, operation number that item is used in, effectivity date and lead time offset.

3) Low-level coding.

4) Same-as-except feature to help create a new but similar bill of material.

5) Maintenance features.

6) Maintaining configuration history.

7) Keeping audit trails and producing error messages.

8) Standard reports.

9) Tying B/M to a specific order (Requirements File).

10) Phantom logic.

Maintenance features bear special examination. You should be able to add items; replace items in a single use and for all uses; delete items in a single use and for all uses; and provide an audit trail that allows you to update data fields before and after the trail.

7/1/95

PARENT NO.	CHANGE	COMPONENT NO.	QTY PER
A105	Delete	D140	1
	Add	D145	1
		B305	1
E282	Change	1054	4
		6200	1
		C284	1

Figure 1: A B/M Audit Trail

The audit trail gives you a history of the changes to a particular item or parent, so you can monitor how and when the product has been changed. The configuration history gives you a complete history of product changes, an important point for product liability issues. A look at the configuration history will tell you what parts were used to make the product at a given point in time.

There are a number of standard reports or displays that are necessary or helpful when restructuring the bill of material.

For a start, you need the single level parts explosion. The multilevel indented display is also important. Single and multi-level where used is necessary. You should be able to generate a pick list from the Requirements File, as we discussed earlier. Your software should also give you a costed bill of material. A list of all parts by classification code is also helpful.

In summary, computers and their software are a means to an end, not the end in itself. If education doesn't precede the software, you're courting, if not disaster, at least disappointment.

Discussion Points

1. Using the software checklist discussed in this chapter, identify weaknesses and strengths in your computer software for managing bills of material.

2. Identify specific enhancements that may be needed in your software to meet each of the internal customer expectations.

3. Identify the audit trails and configuration history capability of your current software.

Chapter 18

The Bill of Material Team

The challenge of revamping the bill of material and implementing a business management system is not in state-of-the-art, latest generation software packages. The first challenge is in getting a critical mass of people from every department to reprioritize their time, work extra hours to design the system and make the critical data accurate.

One of the most important first steps is the formation of a bill of material team to supervise the revamping. As we've said before, the bill of material can't be restructured in a vacuum. The team should have representatives from:

1) Production engineering.
2) Manufacturing engineering.
3) Master scheduling.
4) Order entry.
5) Finance.
6) Quality Assurance.
7) Technical Services (repair).
8) Data Processing.

9) Sales/Marketing.

10) B/M Administration.

11) Production Floor.

12) Purchasing.

All these areas of the company are affected by the bill. They are all legitimate users of the bill of material, and they should all be represented on the bill of material project team.

We want to get all these people together and have them list on a flip chart all the problems—or what they perceive to be the problems—with the bills. Remember that problems with the bills are quality problems, and we want to get those problems out in the open so we can take the first steps to solving them. In fact, the bill of material team could be classified as a Quality Circle chartered with a specific task—make the bill of material meet the total company's expectations, i.e., a high-quality bill of material.

The Importance Of Exchanging Information

Aside from the fact that all these people have a stake in the bill, it's important to have multiple input on the restructuring. The bill of material project team should start exchanging information immediately, breaking down any communications barriers that might exist.

Here's one example of the assignment breakdown of a bill of material project team:

The intent of this policy is to develop a procedure for the creation of a new bill of material. The B/M Project Leader gathers the bill of material task force for the following:

Establish assignments as follows:

Engineering is responsible for:

• Designing and creating the prototype products and the first bill of material.

• Assigning part numbers as necessary and according to company policy.

• Determining the quantity per necessary for each component.

Sales is responsible for:

• Determining options for a product family to be forecast and the percentage of each option.

Purchasing is responsible for:

• The make or buy decisions.

• Determining raw material requirements.

Finance is responsible for:

• Figuring item costs.

Planning is responsible for:

• Determining the planned and scheduled levels.

• Creating phantoms as necessary.

• Creating the planning bills of material.

Production is responsible for:

• Defining the manufacturing process—how the product is really built.

• The type of environment for the product group—volume repetitive, job shop, flow process, etc.

One of the most frequent questions we get in class is who should be on the team, and from what level in the company. The simplest answer to the second part of that question is as high a level as possible. The bill of material is a central item in how the business is to be run. Its importance should be fully understood by executive management. In fact, the ideal situation is to have the CEO of the company chair the first few meetings. Of course, that's not going to happen with a company such as General Motors or Kodak; the alternative is to have a representative of senior management chair that all-important first meeting.

One of the biggest mistakes a company can make is not taking the bill restructuring seriously enough. Without a high level of commitment from the top right down to the bottom, it's simply not going to work. The participation of top management signals that the restructuring of the bill is of utmost importance, important enough to involve the very top level of the company.

The bill of material project team needs to quickly hammer out a bill of material policy. This is basically a statement outlining what the team hopes to accomplish. Here's an example from a "Class A" company.

The Bill of Material Policy

All end items, subassemblies and manufactured components must be identified with a part number and must have a corresponding bill of material.

Bills of material must be entered into the system within five workdays of a part number assignment.

All changes to the bill of material must be documented per the Engineering Change Notice policy.

> The first item of business should be to hammer out a Bill of Material Policy...

Bill of material changes and additions will be audited per the bill of material administrator's job description.

Bill of material accuracy must be maintained at 98 percent or better.

Bill of material accuracy is to be audited by the tracking of unscheduled issues and receipts, random sampling of single level bills of material, reviewing the stockroom pick list and disassembling by Quality Assurance.

Maintenance of the company bill is the responsibility of manufacturing, with input from all the users.

Another method of going about the task is to assemble a list of questions that the task force must answer. The questions serve to point the task force in the right direction regarding the bill. This strategy is a good one, because it allows the task force to collect many of the various department's misgivings about restructuring the bill, then answer those misgivings in a way that satisfies everyone. Let's look at such a list, which includes questions ranging from the most basic to very specific:

Questions and Concerns

1) Do most companies have one bill of material for both product definition and manufacturing control?

2) What data from item and structure maintenance is key and should be retained in history? How long should that history be maintained on-line?

3) Is it necessary for the engineering system to have the

ability to produce bills of material in both part number sequence and assembly, or "as used," sequence?

4) As part of an engineering system's item hold and release function, is it necessary to establish:
- Multiple hold on an item
- Hold using effectivity date
- Hold for a specific production run
- Different hold types (i.e. tooling, engineering, etc.)

5) Should the system permit routings and structures for purchased parts?

6) Must we always create new part numbers when an item's form changes (i.e. when a drill hole is added to a purchased part)?

7) How is the problem of multi-plant operations best handled; where is centralized control over item and bill maintenance desirable? How should the bill of material be structured when components are supplied by one of the satellite companies?

8) Do most companies include expensed items such as welding wire and paint in the bill of material?

9) Should a drawing exist for every variation of a part within a system?

10) Should this manufacturing company use one bill system for both Manufacturing and Engineering? What internal systems need to be in place to accomplish such a change from the current two B/M system? If a single bill concept is adopted, how should the two functions be combined from an internal organization standpoint?

11) Is it possible (or even desirable) for the bill of material to specify how an item is assembled, or is that a function of the routing system?

12) How can the stockroom best facilitate the need to disperse parts to the assembly line by location and time?

13) How best can the bill of material be structured to accommodate a product line that is built to stock, but is made up of a base unit with several different options and shipping bundles? There is also the need to carry the same part for service, but in different colors. There are parts within the system that are used for production as well as service, but when shipped as service parts,

additional items such as paint and decals are added. How can we best accomplish the management of this problem?

These are vital questions, questions that must be addressed before the task force can begin the actual structuring of the bill. Remember, the bill has to address the needs of all the users. If it does not, it's doomed to failure from the very start.

This particular task force then refined the answers to those and other questions into a software checklist that guided them in their software choice.

One important aspect in restructuring the bill is to see that all the various people in the company understand the significance of what is being done. Too often, companies develop a parochial attitude—Manufacturing has little to do with Engineering, which has little to do with Sales, which has nothing to do with Purchasing. The result is that one department doesn't understand the ramifications of its actions on another department. Even a small thing such as Engineering specifying the "quantity per" of a small hardware item as "A/R (as required)" creates ripples throughout the whole company. Purchasing has to translate A/R into a real number to purchase; Finance can't accurately cost the product because no one is really sure what has gone into it; Planning and Scheduling has to hustle around to get in an appropriate number of items to cover A/R—does that mean 100 or one; a thousand or ten?

The First Step

The first step is helping everyone understand how much a planning system and an accurate bill of material means to the company. An engineer, for example, who doesn't understand scheduling problems probably isn't too enthusiastic about or supportive of restructuring the bill.

"We don't have any problems with our bills the way they're structured now," the product engineer says. "Every time I get a customer order, I simply take a red pencil and draw lines through all the parts that aren't required and write in all the parts numbers that are. The stockroom has a complete bill of material for issuing parts, cost accounting can calculate the standard costs, and manufacturing knows which parts are needed to build the product. What else do you need?"

Of course, what isn't understood is how the planning system had to work to get the parts in the stockroom so they were available when the customer order arrived. Sales, Marketing, Finance, Personnel and other departments on the fringes of planning and scheduling activity have similar misconceptions.

People in different departments, from top management to the shop floor, need to see the significance in restructuring the bill. Centrilift's newsletter is an excellent tool to help the ongoing education effort. The more people know, the less likely they are to be a part of the "Silent Majority," the 80 percent who neither help nor hinder, but simply wait and see.

Restructuring a bill of material is not an easy undertaking, but the benefits far outweigh the liabilities.

Discussion Points

1. Identify the potential members of your bill of material structuring team. Which functional areas need to be represented and why?

2. Discuss how the bill of material structuring team could be considered as a Quality Improvement Team.

3. Determine and discuss the specific responsibilities each functional area should have for structuring bills of material.

4. Discuss the key elements of an effective Bill of Material Policy.

5. Discuss each of the thirteen typical questions and concerns and how they should be answered for your business.

6. Have each member of the group independently evaluate how each functional area in your company understands the uses of the bill of material in your company

210   *Structured For Excellence*

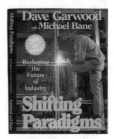

Put
Bills Of Material: Structured For Excellence
to work for your company with the
R.D. Garwood Bill of Material Seminar.

Our hands-on, interactive workshop takes the principles of *Structured For Excellence* and brings them down to your shop floor. The workshop addresses the role of the bill of material in manufacturing companies that are process, job shop, flow or repetitive. The principles and techniques have been proven in companies with assembled products, pharmaceutical companies, chemical manufacturers, engineer-to-order companies and many, many others. You'll get specific examples from a variety of companies, materials to help you in the implementation process and the benefit of more than 25 years' experience in bills of material consulting.

Topics Covered:

- Ten Critical Requirements
- Accuracy: A Quality Issue
- Shallow Bills
- Process/Routing Sheets
- Software Requirements Checklist
- What to Include on the Bills
- Cost Accounting Considerations
- Engineering vs. Manufacturing Bills
- Modularizing Bills: When and How
- Planning Bills
- Order Entry Considerations
- Managing Bill Changes
- New Products and Special Orders
- Steps to Restructuring
- Responsibility for Restructuring
- Part Numbers
- Planning Engineering Capacity
- Bills of Material

You'll Learn To:

- Apply TQM to Bills of Material
- Use Planning Bills to Reduce Forecast Variability
- Maintain a "Defect-Free" Bill of Material
- Reduce the "Total" Cost of Engineering Changes
- Manage Engineering Changes
- Flatten Bills to 2-3 Levels
- Modularize Bills
- Include Tooling and Supplies on Bills
- Create Planning Bills
- Maintain One Company Bill
- Eliminate Unnecessary Bills
- Improve the New Product Development Process

FOR MORE INFORMATION, CALL 800-241-6653 OR 404-952-2976

 R.D. Garwood, Inc.
"Reshaping The Future Of Industry"
P.O. Box 28755
Atlanta, GA 30358-0755